C4 585326 00 58

NEWCASTLE LIBRARIES

WITHDRAWN FROM
NEWCASTLE UPON TYNE
CITY LIBRARIES

SUSAN WES[...] [...]uschka's philosophy and practices. Sh[...] [...]master herb grower before becoming a sales representative for Dr. Hauschka products in the 1970s, and went on to become a licensed aesthetician and the president of Dr. Hauschka Skin Care, Inc., in 1993. She lives in Jamestown, Rhode Island, with her husband and three children.

JAN 20[...]
AUG 20[...]
S NOV 20[...]
[...] 20[...]

Aw[...]ening Beauty
[...] Dr. Hauschka Way

D0320541

Awakening Beauty
the Dr. Hauschka Way

Susan West Kurz
with Tom Monte

CLAIRVIEW

NEWCASTLE LIBRARIES

C458532600	
Bertrams	23/11/2009
646.72	£16.99

Clairview Books
Hillside House, The Square
Forest Row, East Sussex
RH18 5ES

www.clairviewbooks.com

Published by Clairview Books 2008

First published in the United Kingdom
in hardback by Clairview Books 2006

Copyright © 2006 Susan West Kurz

Susan West Kurz asserts the moral right to be
identified as the author of this work

All rights reserved. No part of this publication may be
reproduced, stored in a retrieval system, or transmitted,
in any form or by any means, electronic, mechanical,
photocopying or otherwise, without the prior
permission of the publishers

A catalogue record for this book is available
from the British Library

ISBN 978 1 905570 16 4

Interior and cover design by Jennifer K. Beal;
cover for paperback modified by Andrew Morgan

Front cover photograph © Veer;
back cover photos by Furnald/Gray
except left, courtesy WALA Heilmittel GmbH

Printed and bound in China
by 1010 Printing International Ltd.

contents

Introduction

"If only you would smile, you would be beautiful," my mother sometimes said to me when I was a young girl. As I grew older, other adults continued to point out characteristics that if changed would make me more beautiful. Eventually, I took over the job of critiquing my appearance. I often told myself that if my nose were straighter, or my eyes less deep-set, or my hips a little smaller, I would indeed be beautiful.

I emerged from childhood unable to see my beauty. And because I couldn't see it, I couldn't appreciate being me. You could say that my perception of my beauty—and my relationship to myself—was diminished or even wounded.

As I matured, I came to realize that I was not alone. Most of my peers—even those whom I considered beautiful by any standard—were often unable to see and appreciate their beauty.

Recently, I asked a few very attractive women if they considered themselves beautiful. One told me, "Oh no, I'm not beautiful. Are you kidding?" Another said, "People tell me I'm beautiful, but I don't feel beautiful." Yet another woman answered by asking, "Do you think I'm beautiful?" "Yes, I do," I said. She hugged me, and when we let go of each other, I could see tears in her eyes.

It took me many years to heal something fundamental inside myself so that I could recognize and be grateful for my beauty. As I came to know myself, I eventually realized that beauty is a luminous and joyful state of self-love that lives inside all of us. This inner beauty has the power to affect our outer beauty by improving the health of our skin, transforming the shape and movement of our bodies, and giving off a radiance that inspires those around us. As Oscar Wilde once wrote, "One does not see anything until one sees its beauty." That's especially true when applied to ourselves.

As a society, our relationship with beauty is in crisis. We are told that beauty exists only in certain images and only at certain ages. The media assault us with images that lead us away from our own unique beauty. They encourage us to try to look like someone else rather than become and accept more of who we truly are. While adults suffer from such messages, they are especially damaging to children, who want so desperately to be loved, approved of, and seen as beautiful.

Equally damaging is the message that beauty is unattainable beyond a certain age. We worship youth and deny the aging process, even though young people are often inexperienced, immature, full of conflict, and lacking in emotional depth. We are often unable to see the beauty in spiritual growth, maturity, and wisdom. As I show later in this book, each stage of life offers us unique opportunities to experience our own inner and outer beauty.

This book is about healing your inner and outer beauty. By adopting the healing and lifestyle practices I recommend, you will see and experience both your inner and outer beauty; you will nourish and develop it; and you will see it come shining forth.

Healing the Skin

A big part of healing your inner beauty is healing your skin and restoring its health, vitality, and glow. I have been working in the skin care and beauty industry for the past twenty-five years. I have been an esthetician, a teacher of skin care, a businesswoman, and, today, the president of Dr. Hauschka Skin Care, Inc. Over the course of that quarter-century, I have learned a great deal about what the skin needs to be healthy and beautiful. Unfortunately, many of today's products do more harm than good or simply address symptoms without restoring the skin's underlying health and function.

No other organ is so intimately connected to our appearance and our beauty than our skin. When we damage our skin, we diminish our beauty and change the way we feel about ourselves overall. Therefore, healing our skin is an essential part of healing our beauty.

Rudolf Hauschka developed essential principles to address healthy skin and healing beauty. A twentieth-century Austrian chemist, Dr. Hauschka created a company in the 1950s whose goals were to heal humanity and the earth. Hauschka wanted to create a new form of medicine, one that healed illness and its symptoms but also restored the health and function of the overall organism without damaging side effects. Medicine should treat the entire person, Hauschka believed, by boosting the body's healing forces, including the subtle energies that animate it and restore its health. After twenty years of trial and error, Hauschka developed a method of extracting plants' active ingredients as well as their vital energies. He then began supplying these plant-based medicines to doctors and healers throughout Europe, with remarkable results.

In the 1960s, he was joined by Austrian-born esthetician Elisabeth Sigmund, who specialized in creating medicinal substances that healed the skin and restored its underlying functions, such as its capacity to replenish cells and keep its underlying fibers moist and full. By creating such healing formulas, Sigmund hoped to incorporate skin care into mainstream medicine.

Together, Hauschka and Sigmund created a line of herbal medicine skin care products. Each is made from high-potency medicinal plants that have been grown biodynamically. (Biodynamics is a form of agriculture that far exceeds organic standards in its purity and reverence for nature.) The plants are harvested by hand at dawn, when their essential oils and life energies are strongest. They are processed using Hauschka's rhythmical extraction method, which preserves and enhances the plants' vital forces. This combination of medicinal properties and botanicals has a powerful healing effect on the skin.

I was first introduced to the Dr. Hauschka Skin Care products and philosophy in 1972, when I apprenticed at the Meadowbrook Herb Garden in Rhode Island, where I learned to grow medicinal and culinary herbs for food, medicine, and cosmetics. The man who guided me in this work imported and sold the Dr. Hauschka Skin Care line. It wasn't long before I became an independent sales representative, initially selling Dr. Hauschka to friends and family, including my boyfriend, later my husband, actor J. T. Walsh.

above Author Susan Kurz was introduced to Dr. Hauschka Skin Care products and philosophy in 1972.

below Austrian chemist Dr. Rudolf Hauschka (1891–1969) cofounded WALA Heilmittel in Eckwälden, Germany—a company whose goals were to heal humanity and the earth.

opposite Elisabeth Sigmund, groundbreaking esthetician and cofounder of Dr. Hauschka Skin Care, developed products and treatments to inspire beauty by supporting health.

Before appearing in movies, J. T. acted on the stage, where his sensitive Irish skin was subjected each night to harsh makeup and hot lights. He suffered constantly from a variety of skin problems.

Using the Dr. Hauschka principles and training as my guide, I set up an intensive treatment program for him that included healing skin care applications, herbal teas, and organic food. It wasn't long before his skin was both healthy and glowing. Later, J. T. worked with well-known makeup artist Leslie Fuller, who studied the Dr. Hauschka methods and used them to care for his skin before and after applying his makeup. Leslie, like many Hollywood makeup artists, introduced the Dr. Hauschka products and principles to other film stars. A-list celebrities, professional makeup artists, and Hollywood stylists have long embraced Dr. Hauschka's botanical products, attracted by their extraordinary results and the company's thirty-five-year commitment to purity, therapy, and luxury.

Guided by the Dr. Hauschka principles, I am going to show you how to choose skin care products that, when combined with other healing behaviors, can restore the beauty of your skin and heal it of disorders from which it may suffer, including acne, rosacea, and premature aging. In many cases, I will show you how to create your own powerful herbal formulations from plant-based ingredients that are inexpensive and easily obtainable. By using these recommendations, you can transform your appearance and restore the glow and beauty to your skin.

The Dr. Hauschka way is more than a medicinal approach to the skin, or what you put on your face. It offers practical guidance for slowing down, finding your natural rhythms, and discovering the true inner beauty that already lives inside you.

The skin, like all your organs, is infused with an energy that permeates its cells and gives it health and beauty. That underlying life force, if you will, is intimately connected to your inner beauty. If you allow yourself, you can perceive this underlying life force when you touch your face. The connection between your hands and your spirit is so strong that it makes you forget the skin of your face or the bones beneath the skin. By enhancing your connection to your inner life, your beauty can be experienced—first by you, and then by anyone with whom you wish to share it.

That inner connection is strengthened by spending time in nature, whose healing rhythms bring calm and renewal to our own lives. Nature is not only a great source of external beauty but also a nurturing force that can restore physical and emotional health and beauty, as well.

Actor J. T. Walsh

What's So Special About Being Beautiful?

All of us want to be beautiful, whether we admit it or not. Our desire for beauty is woven into our genes. My ten-year-old-daughter, Rossibel, asks me if she is beautiful, and she is instantly reassured and deeply satisfied when I tell her she truly is. My mother telephoned recently to tell me that someone in her doctor's office couldn't believe she is ninety. The man said she didn't look a day over eighty! She was thrilled by this comment because it made her feel beautiful.

What is this mysterious pull that beauty has on us? Why do beautiful people attract us—or, to put it another way, why do you become such a powerful magnet for people and opportunities when you are beautiful? The reason beauty draws us near is because it arises from love, which is itself the most nourishing and desired force in life. Beauty is the consequence of love, and therefore announces the presence of love, which we are ultimately drawn to.

Making yourself more beautiful is dependent on giving yourself more love. Loving yourself is deeply nourishing and healing. It satisfies you in ways that no other form of love can. When we love ourselves, a mysterious array of chemicals and emotions align, making us physically and emotionally balanced, even radiant. When we love ourselves on a daily basis, our beauty grows very rapidly.

A beautiful woman or man, someone who fundamentally loves herself or himself, exhibits a special type of grace, balance, and integrity that demonstrates for all to see the human potential to be whole.

What Does It Mean to Be Whole?

We hear a great deal about this mysterious state of wholeness that is the basis for health and beauty. What is wholeness, and how can we achieve it? The simplest way to describe it is as a way of living that allows us to love more and more of who we are.

Most of us have been trained to see certain aspects of ourselves in a negative light. We may view our entire physical appearance, or some part of it— our nose or mouth, for example—as unattractive and even ugly. In the same way, we may have been trained to reject aspects of our character as well. Many of us have learned to see our anger, sexuality, power, or desire to perform as negative. Becoming whole is learning to embrace those parts of us that have been rejected or denied and bringing them back into a state of love, compassion, and acceptance. This embrace has a healing effect on our bodies and minds. We become more relaxed inside our skin and more at peace with who we are. When we accept our power as a great gift, we see

Chapter 1

Restoring Beauty
with Rhythm

One of the most powerful ways to establish peace in your life and restore your beauty is to live in harmony with your inner rhythms. Inside you is an internal clock whose pulsations determine when you should wake up in the morning, when you should eat, when your energy levels are peaking, and when it's time for you to rest. These rhythms determine the ebbs and flows of your life.

Most of us live by rhythms that are not our own. Our daily schedules are shaped by the demands of our environment, whether they come from the people we love, our work, or everyday life. Consequently, each day can seem like a psychic tug of war between our own rhythms and those of others. Many of us come to believe that our desires cannot be met unless we have major changes in our lives, like altering important relationships or leaving our jobs. Meanwhile, we go on postponing the inner cry for help and care, which causes us to lose contact with our hearts and age prematurely and, ultimately, causes our beauty to dry up and wither away.

The beauty of your internal rhythmic clock is that it's always there and can always be returned to. No matter how demanding and chaotic your days are, you can still come home to the deeply nurturing beats that are your real life. By practicing listening to and, as much as possible, living by your own inner rhythms, you can find the beauty that is waiting to be discovered.

Your internal rhythms are real—as real as your heartbeat, the rise and fall of your breathing, and the ebb and flow of your hormones. In fact, all biological functions occur rhythmically.

Out of your unique biological cycles come your energy patterns and moods. These waves determine when you are at your best and when you need rest and recovery. There are periods in your day, week, and month when you have the energy to give, to love, and to nourish others, just as there are periods when your inner rhythms urge you to rest and engage in self-care.

Rhythm is so subtle, yet all-pervasive, that we can easily overlook it. Nature, with her cycles of light and darkness, warmth and cold, stillness and movement, is our biological source and our most immediate example of rhythm.

Each of us uses rhythm to create some degree of order and stability in our lives. You wake up at a certain hour, eat a meal, go to work or perform certain activities at specific hours, come home again at night, and finally fall asleep, only to wake up each morning relatively renewed. Rhythm is the basis for order, and order is the basis for stability, predictability, and good health. Thus, rhythm is an antidote to our fear of the unexpected.

We are beings in search of the deep rhythms of our inner lives. The more we listen to our inner music and act in accordance with it, the more we engage in behaviors that nourish us, promote our health, and restore our beauty.

The Warning Signs That You Are Living Against Your Rhythms

Somehow in recent years, serving others—at home with friends and at our jobs—even when it means exhausting ourselves, has become the basis for "being a good person." In doing this, we refuse to acknowledge our physical and psychological need for balance. Our bodies and minds need both rest and a certain amount of care and play to be healthy and happy. When we sacrifice too much, we become exhausted, angry, and fearful. Most of us don't realize this until we are utterly spent, miserable, and in jeopardy of losing our health.

Whenever you are exhausted but give more than is healthy for you, or simply more than you have, your inner world sends out warning signals that appear as either fear or anger or both. Your inner guidance system is telling you to slow down, to back away from life's demands, to rest and recover your connection to yourself.

People who are chronically angry often fail to realize that their inner guidance systems are telling them to come back to themselves and start meeting their own needs. Too much of these angry and fearful emotions can poison our health and strip us of our beauty. These people's inner wisdom is pleading with them: "Pay attention! You need rest. You need time to be alone and time to be with those you love and who love you. You need to have fun, to dance in the sun and walk in the rain. Fill up again. You're empty!"

Therapists working with people who have suffered from substance abuse have coined the acronym HALT—hungry, angry, lonely, tired—to help people recognize the cues that make us vulnerable to self-destructive behaviors. The more time you spend in communion with your own rhythms, the less isolated you will feel—and the more power you have to diffuse the HALT emotions.

As powerful as anger and fear can be, many of us fail to respect them as early warnings of depletion and exhaustion. When we don't listen to these early signals, stronger messages are needed. One of the gentler ways our inner nature forces us to slow down is by allowing us to contract the common cold. Lying on our back, we have no choice but to reconnect with our inner rhythms. We know, if only intuitively, that those rhythms are the source of healing and health. We must relax and give in to the gentle embrace of those rhythms until our body has fully recovered.

Rather than being seen as a reason to reconnect to our need for rest and self-care, the common cold is widely interpreted as a nuisance, something to be conquered with drugs. The pharmaceutical industry has convinced us that rather than listen to our inner rhythms and respond appropriately, we should take a pill or a potion and deny our need for rest and recovery. This is just one of many ways in which modern life steers us away from our innate desire for self-love.

Drifting too far from one's inner rhythms can be dangerous. Even before catastrophe strikes, we suffer a host of losses. We age rapidly and become tired, angry, and fearful, all of which rob us of our beauty. For those who deny the subtle warnings, more extreme measures can arise, such as accidents or illness. How many times have we heard of people who were pushing themselves too hard and then experienced a breakdown in a relationship or got into a car accident because they failed to pay attention? Or of friends who experienced so much stress they became seriously ill or had a heart attack.

Your rhythms support your life and cause it to unfold. By understanding and knowing your rhythms, you develop your sense of self, an ever-increasing capacity for genuine love, and an ever-unfolding beauty.

Discovering Your Rhythms Is Easier Than You May Think

Your beauty, your health, and much of your youthful vitality can be recovered simply by listening to, and returning to, the gentle waves of your inner world that is alive with feelings and thoughts. When we integrate our emotions, thoughts, and actions, we live in harmony with our rhythms. Granted, it's impossible to do this all the time, but the more we bring harmony to our inner lives and outer behaviors, the greater our health and beauty will become.

The first step in this process is simply to experience our own subtle inner feelings. There are many ways to do this. One of the easier ways, for me, is simply to sit in the sun with my cat in my lap. Lucy's deep restfulness is contagious. Her meditative state passes to me. My body relaxes as I look out my window onto my garden and the tall trees that surround my house. Doing "nothing," especially when you do it in the sun or by a window on a rainy day, is a beautiful and much-needed experience.

above Pets' restful, meditative state can be contagious.

As I sit in my garden, the demands of my life retreat. My inner being seems to connect with the natural outside world. In the stillness, I feel the life of the trees, bushes, and flowers rise to meet me. I feel my own life rise in return. Something deep, serene, and beautiful stirs inside me and spreads through my inner world. My breath becomes deeper and more rhythmic. The tension in my lower back, pelvis, and legs releases, and my breath flows deeply into my body. Soon my heart opens and I feel at peace with my world. Time has stopped. My body is deeply relaxed, and I feel whole and happy. I am being healed and nourished in ways that nothing else in my life can provide.

Another simple way to experience your inner rhythms and to bring order to them is to create order in your environment. Often when I feel my life is getting out of control, I organize my office, clean a room in my house, or arrange a drawer or my jewelry box. It sounds mundane, but the act of creating order around me puts me in touch with the order within me. It also helps me avoid trying to control everyone else around me.

Much of life is chaotic, nonsensical, and draining. Rhythm awareness and inner wisdom create a sense of order and peace to combat these negative circumstances. Beauty is your birthright. You will always have the potential to be beautiful as long as you act in harmony with your rhythms.

Practicing Healing Beauty

Your face and body reflect your physical and emotional health. You carry stresses, fears, and anger that alter your inner life and affect your health, happiness, and physical appearance. If you are to be truly beautiful and fulfilled, you must be actively engaged in healing your inner conflicts.

Healing is very different from curing, just as the work of healers is very different from that of medical doctors. *Healing* is the act of ridding the body of the conditions that create and support disease. Most of the illnesses people suffer from today arise primarily from lifestyle-related causes, such as stress, diet, and lack of exercise. Changes in these areas can eliminate many illnesses.

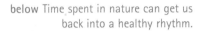

below Time spent in nature can get us back into a healthy rhythm.

Ridding the body of the underlying causes of disease, while at the same time promoting good health, is the act of healing. Healing requires your active participation. As you engage in healing behaviors—exercising more, taking more time for yourself, eating a more healthful diet—you are changed for the better. In anthroposophy, your efforts to promote good health and a better life are known as *salutogenesis,* a word that is derived from the Latin *salus,* meaning health, and the Greek *genesis,* meaning origin. In the next few chapters, I will show you how to use salutogenesis to promote the health and beauty of your skin.

The healing approach to health care is unlike what medical doctors do today. When a doctor tries to cure you of an illness, he or she focuses mainly on the symptoms of your disease. The belief is that when the symptoms are eliminated, the disease has been effectively treated. Drugs are often used to suppress the symptoms, but often the underlying causes of the disease remain in place, which means that stronger and more numerous medications are needed to eliminate its symptoms.

left A warm bath is relaxing and soothing and reconnects us to our personal rhythms.

In most cases, healing and curing can be administered in combination to effectively treat disease. But in order to truly eliminate an illness or any condition that causes you distress, healing is always necessary, especially since most drugs do not address the underlying causes of your problems. There are real-life reasons for your anger, fear, or chronic stress. All of us attempt to repress painful memories. But when we allow certain painful emotions or memories back into our consciousness through the act of self-healing, we are able to welcome them back with acceptance and love, thus becoming more whole. This results in deeper inner peace and tranquillity. You have the strength and resources to confront these problems. But before you can effectively address the challenges you face, you need two forms of support you may not yet have. The first is a compassionate relationship with yourself, achieved by responding to your rhythms and emotions. The second is a healer to help you find these rhythms and, eventually, your authentic beauty.

To find a nonjudgmental healer who is right for you, start by asking friends if they know of a massage therapist or a Reiki practitioner. If your friends don't know anyone, explore day spas in your community that offer massage or other forms of healing touch. You can also ask your doctor, or simply choose someone from the telephone book or local newspaper. You may also want to find out if there is a local school for massage, shiatsu, acupressure, acupuncture, or some other form of therapeutic touch in your area. These types of schools are always looking for volunteers on whom their students can practice and learn their trade. Volunteers usually get a full body treatment for a fraction of the regular cost.

Be clear about the kind of person you are looking for. Will you be more comfortable with a woman or a man? How old should the person be? Remember: The most important characteristics are that she or he be free of judgment and possess a healing manner and touch. Once you find a healer, go regularly.

Use Rhythm to Reinforce Your Healing Practice

It's all well and good to have a massage, acupuncture, or holistic skin care treatment, but one session will not create any lasting effect. The reason is that the impact of the treatment will dissipate with time. In order for gentle forms of therapy such as healing touch, massage, or acupuncture to transform you, their effects must be reinforced with regular treatments. If you want to maximize the power of those treatments, use rhythm to reinforce their healing effects.

Let's say you see a practitioner weekly, or even once a month. Schedule your appointments for the same day each week, or each month, at the same hour—for example, 3 P.M. every Thursday, or 3 P.M. on the third Thursday of each month. Your body, mind, and spirit will then become aware that they are getting a boost of healing energy in a rhythmic, or wavelike, pattern. With continued treatments, that pattern will be reinforced, deepened, and strengthened. Soon, your internal rhythms will rise automatically as the time approaches for your treatment, thus boosting your self-healing forces and conditioning your body to heal. That healing will show in your skin, your face, and your body.

A series of healing baths puts you in touch with your inner life and, at the same time, helps heal the imbalances that may be causing distress. Make a ritual of this practice and see if it doesn't also stir feelings of deep inner peace.

Once you have had your bath, rested, and written in your diary, try doing a simple exercise created by Rudolf Steiner to speed healing and spiritual development. Remember the day's details in reverse order—that is, start recalling your day from the evening to afternoon to morning to dawn. Steiner maintained that by doing this exercise, we digest and integrate the events, emotions, and insights of the day. In effect, we get more out of the day and, by extension, our lives. We also deepen the lessons learned that day, which makes them more useful and available to us as we go through life. The exercise sounds simple, but it takes practice. Do it while sitting in a chair. Usually, you'll get sleepy long before you have fully reviewed the events that took place that day. That's fine. It's a good way to allow yourself to get tired and prepare for sleep.

As you practice this exercise, you'll increasingly see yourself in a more objective light because you'll witness yourself from an outside perspective, discovering things about your behavior you never saw before. For example, many people see the ways in which they unconsciously block effective communication, or how they fail to notice the love someone is trying to give them. As you witness yourself struggling to deal with some issue, you also awaken your compassion for yourself, which is extremely healing.

Baths to Cleanse the Soul

One of my favorite rhythmic practices is to take a series of healing and restorative baths. I choose a particular night each week, say Wednesday, and a particular hour, say 8 P.M., and maintain this rhythm for seven weeks. After the bath, I rest for about twenty minutes, or as long as I was in the bath, and then write in my diary for another half hour to an hour. This healing practice can be enhanced by adding essential oil concentrates to each bath. I choose an essential oil to balance my temperament or mood at the time, or one that is appropriate to the season.

The philosophical movement of anthroposophy maintains that very small quantities of a medicinal substance could be charged with energy and thus made more powerful by shaking or stirring the medicine repeatedly. This practice, which originated with homeopathy, came to be known as *potentization* or *succussion*. The sudden shaking—succussion—charges the medicine with a jolt of energy that catalyzes the medicine and makes it more potent.

You can give your bath greater healing potential by gently circulating the water in the shape of a figure 8 until vortexes appear in the water. As you circulate the water, notice the change in the feeling and texture of the water as you potentize it. The water feels more silky, homogeneous, and slightly more viscous. It's as if the water suddenly became more integrated and powerful.

In nature, pure, clean water is always moving in rhythmical patterns, as within a river or a brook. You can bring this same healing approach to your own bathing rituals. Masaru Emoto, a renowned Japanese scientist and author of the book *The Hidden Messages in Water,* discovered that water is highly sensitive to words, vibrations, and even thoughts. Emoto found that words have different effects on water depending on their meaning, and showed that when water is quickly frozen into crystals after it is exposed to life-supporting words such as *love* and *gratitude,* the crystals are stunning in their beauty and order.

Here are five types of essential oils that can be used in a healing bath cycle to cleanse and harmonize your spirit.

Lavender Oil

Lavender relaxes muscles and calms and soothes the nervous system. Any time you are under stress or on the edge of anger or fear, take a lavender bath to bring you back into balance and harmony. Lavender cools hot skin conditions such as inflamed capillaries and rashes. It relaxes and moistens dry skin, soothes nerves, and reduces redness and itching. Because it cools, lavender is great for hot summer nights. It is a perfect evening bath.

Lemon Oil

Essential oil of lemon refreshes and restores us when we suffer from physical exhaustion. Used as a healing tonic in virtually every culture, fresh-squeezed lemon or its essential oil refreshes and tones the skin, restoring its youthful glow. Lemon juice or lemon oil is also used as an astringent to close oozing skin or treat rashes and allergies that cause too much moisture in the skin and sinuses. Lemon is an ideal bath for spring and summer.

Rosemary Oil

Rosemary promotes circulation. It warms, rejuvenates, and relaxes the body. Take a rosemary bath if you have chronically cold hands and feet or when you just can't get warm. Rosemary also strengthens and warms the spirit. It is traditionally used when we feel weak, shy, or afraid, or suffer from figurative cold feet and simply can't face the world. Rosemary helps us relax when we've been working too hard for too long or feel overwhelmed by our problems. Rosemary is also used to treat sallow, listless skin because it brightens and restores color. All of this makes rosemary ideal for a fall and winter series of baths. Because it is so energizing, it's also a wonderful way to begin the day.

Sage Oil

Sage is used traditionally as a
smudge to cleanse the spirit before
sacred rituals. A sage bath neutralizes hostile or negative thoughts
and emotions, drawing out anger,
fear, and sadness from the tissues.
It soothes and cleanses the internal
rhythms of heavy or dark emotions
and thoughts. A sage bath also can
be used to treat body acne.

Spruce Oil

Spruce reins in emotions that seem
out of control. It soothes and opens
the lungs and the entire rhythmic
system, restoring us when we feel
emotionally exhausted, spent, and
burned out. Spruce is an ideal bath
for late winter and early spring, as
well as whenever your lungs or
sinuses are congested.

Healing Is As Simple As a Walk in the Park

Here's a simple prescription to reduce stress and fear and to restore sanity: Walk in a park or be in nature at least once a week. The healing becomes stronger when you take the nature cure more often. Nature's loving rhythms and healing energies are still the most rejuvenating forces. A few days at the ocean or in a cabin by a lake brings us back to our senses. A walk in the mountains or some time by a river awakens the subtle cadences of our inner world, restoring the beauty within. After a few days in nature's rhythmic embrace, you will begin to feel tension melt away, allowing the subtle energies within you to surface. In no time, your physical and emotional health is rejuvenated and your beauty restored.

Take nature's cure today by choosing a day each week to eat lunch in the park or spend twenty minutes or more walking amid the trees with a friend—or alone. Notice the trees in every season. Look at the flowers as they are gently shaken by the wind and seem to dance and call out for your attention. Take the colors of nature into your spirit so that they enrich and transform your inner life. Breathe deeply and exhale the tension from your body and mind. Feel your inner rhythms rise in the presence of such beauty.

Exercise for Rhythm, Not for Fitness

When we think of exercise, most of us think of pain. We have been trained to think of some idealized state of fitness as the goal toward which we should strive. However, understanding your body's rhythm changes can change your approach to exercise. Your new goal is to come into harmony with your internal environment; this will dramatically reduce your stress levels, give you a deep experience of peace, and restore your sense of self, allowing you to think more clearly. As a result, you will have a healthier perspective on the circumstances of your life and make smarter decisions.

With rhythm as your goal, walk with the intention of harmonizing your speed and distance with how you feel inside. Today you may be in a reflective mood. If so, walk slowly and allow yourself to feel and think deeply. You may be in that reflective state for a week or many weeks. Walk to support your reflective state of mind. If tomorrow you feel light and joyful, walk lightly and joyfully. Next week, you may be full of energy. Perhaps you will want to walk at a faster pace. You may even want to run for a distance. Go for it. But when your body says "Slow down or rest," listen to it. And when your body says, "Let's start up again," do so. Practice moving according to your inner guidance.

Both rhythm and exercise function as waves. The rising part of the wave is when energy is being expended in ever-greater quantities until the expenditure reaches its peak. The declining part of the wave is when energy is being burned more slowly until you reach a point of rest. During the burn phase, muscles are working hard and tissues are breaking down. During the resting phase, you are gathering energy, healing the body, and rebuilding tissues. We see this wave pattern clearly when we consider the effects of exercise on our muscles and bones. During the workout phase, muscle and bone tissue are stressed and broken down. During the recovery phase, muscle and bone are healed and rebuilt; in many cases, both become stronger than they were before we exercised.

Exercise is a threefold phenomenon: energy expenditure rises; energy expenditure slows; rest occurs, and energy recovery takes place. By engaging consciously in each aspect of the rhythmic nature of exercise, we promote the body's ability to heal, rebuild, and recover. Therefore, when you walk, or do any exercise, remain conscious of your inner rhythms. The speed and distance you walk should reflect your inner world, not a fantasy image of fitness. Expend the energy that your body can give up. Give your body as much rest as it needs to fully recover.

In this way, you can make walking a meditation—light and happy sometimes, contemplative and reflective at others, angry and full of turmoil occasionally. Let your rhythms guide your exercise patterns.

You might also want to consider doing other activities that expand your connection to your internal rhythms. Eurythmy, which means beautiful, harmonious movement, is a new art form; inspired by Rudolf Steiner, it is both a dancelike and a therapeutic exercise. It is designed to foster an intimate connection among body, emotions, and spirit through expanding and contracting movements. It is taught at Waldorf Schools—the schools inspired by Steiner to develop the whole child—and any anthroposophical foundation in your local community. Yoga, which means union of body, mind, and spirit, is an exercise designed to put you in touch with your inner rhythms. Tai chi chuan, which means the harmonious movement of the life force, or chi, is a martial art based on rhythmic movements. It is a meditative dance whose purpose is to attune you to your own internal waves and energies. Other martial arts can do the same, as long as the movement is a direct reflection of your own internal rhythms.

The added benefit of the rhythmic approach to exercise is that it actually results in fitness and improved health. Even small amounts of exercise, especially walking, dramatically improve healing. A study done by Harvard researchers and published in the March 2001 issue of the *Journal of the American Medical Association* showed that women who walk just one hour a week have half the risk of heart disease and heart attack as those who are sedentary. Other research has shown that regular, moderate walking reduces the risk of heart disease, cancer, diabetes, and high blood pressure in both men and women. Regular walking dramatically reduces a woman's risk of breast cancer. The point is to move—walk, dance, or perform some other activity. Do it for the pleasure, not the perfection.

Yoga is an exercise based on your inner rhythms.

Zen Exercise:
Do Nothing and Gain the Entire World

In addition to physical exercise, schedule at least twenty minutes each week in which your only activity is to sit comfortably in your home, or in your garden, and feel your feelings.

There are some rules for this activity, however. First, you cannot go to sleep. Second, you cannot watch television, write, or do any other activity. Third, if you find that you are in a highly emotional state, allow your emotions to emerge into clarity until you feel compassion for yourself. Once you achieve this, your inner world will be clear, and the love and healing energies will flow.

At the very least, this is a time of profound rest and deep healing. But this practice also reveals all types of inspiration and guidance from deep within you. Many things become clear. If you are struggling with a major decision, the answer will come to you. By doing nothing, you allow the subtle wisdom within you to rise and guide you. Along with inspiration will come clarity, enthusiasm, and the courage to follow the path before you.

A Meditative Ritual at the Start of
Your Day and Before Each Meal

One of the most powerful antidotes to chaos and fear is the restoration of a union with ourselves through meditation. Any form of meditation or reflective contemplation will work if you make a direct and personal connection to the practice. You may recite a prayer you learned in childhood or engage in a ritual or meditation you learned as an adult. The idea is to direct your mind to a particular image or set of words that uplifts you.

There need not be any prescribed time limit, either. Meditation can take as little as five minutes or much longer, if you prefer. But try to do it every morning at the same time and preferably in the same place whenever possible. If you feel it is appropriate, make a simple altar in a peaceful part of your home, or conduct your practice in your garden, under a great tree, or in a private meadow.

By engaging in a meditative or ritual act at the same time each morning, you add to your internal rhythm, which gives your prayer a powerful humility and a simple beauty. At the same time, you are training your body, mind, and spirit to open up at the same hour each day to the mystery and power that

Here are a few universal prayers and meditations you can use each morning as a start to your practice.

Waking up this morning, I smile,
Twenty-four brand-new hours
    are before me.
I vow to live fully in each
    moment
And to look at all beings with
    eyes of Compassion.

        —A prayer by Thich Nhat Hanh

Surrender to nature's beauty; I
    find myself in her
The beauty of the world
    strengthens and empowers me
Beauty unites spirit with my
    being
I bear summer in me like a seed

        —From *The Calendar of the Soul*
        by Rudolf Steiner, translated by
        Christopher Bamford

Beauty behind me,
Beauty all around me,
Above me and below me hovers
    the beautiful.
I'm surrounded by beauty; I am
    immersed in it.
In my youth, I am aware of it,
And in old age, I shall walk
    quietly the beautiful path.
In beauty it is begun. In beauty it
    is ended.

        —Navaho prayer

underlies the entire universe. When done consistently, this act becomes the foundation of your day and, eventually, your life. Your practice becomes the spiritual haven to which you retreat in times of difficulty, the place where you go to give thanks for all that you have been given.

Many people prefer to pray or meditate in movement, such as sacred dance, yoga, or a martial art such as tai chi chuan. If any one of these practices gives you the experience of connection and faith, then by all means engage in it daily.

If you like, you can make a small expression of thanks before each meal as well. In our house, we light a candle at dinner each night and say a prayer in which we thank the sun and the earth for our food. This small ritual allows us to relax and prepares our body to receive food. It also reminds us to be grateful for what we have been given. You can do this unobtrusively, without calling attention to yourself. Simply bow your head, close your eyes, and take a moment to be aware of your gratitude.

The Four Faces Within

Choosing the bath, exercise, or meditative practice that's right for you depends on your ability to see your current imbalances. One of the most effective tools for self-examination and rebalancing is the Four Temperaments.

The Four Temperaments is a typology, or ancient form of psychology, for understanding the four different personality types. Created by the ancient Greeks, who associated each personality type with an aspect of nature, the Four Temperaments has been studied throughout history and refined by leading psychologists and philosophers, including the twentieth-century philosopher and scientist Rudolf Steiner.

Each of the four personality types has a positive and a negative pole. Each type can become imbalanced and turn into its own source of stress and conflict. At that point, we need to figure out how the imbalance arose and what we can do to right the ship again and regain our rhythm and balance.

It's important to keep in mind that we all possess these four temperaments. We tend to be more comfortable with one or two of them, but all four are within us. The more we explore each temperament, the more we can navigate in and out of each one, depending on the demands of the situation we are facing. That is a kind of mastery that each of us is striving for. The more wedded we are to a single temperament, the more likely we are to suffer the imbalances associated with that way of being.

Choleric Temperament: Let's Get It Done—Now!

When you are in the choleric temperament, you are a doer and a leader. You take on challenges and get things done. You're active and focused on your work. You meet deadlines; you complete tasks. During such periods, you often have great stamina, lots of energy, and determination. You're resolute. You tend to forget your personal concerns and concentrate instead on the details of the job or challenge facing you. Hence, significant accomplishments are possible.

Physically, you radiate confidence and power. There's a certain authority in your walk and presence. You're grounded, practical, and sure of yourself. All of this shows in your appearance.

The ancient Greeks associated this temperament with the fire element—and, indeed, when you are in the choleric temperament, your emotions tend to be fiery. But as stress builds, your determination can turn into stubbornness. Your attention to detail and insistence on making things right can become the basis for frustration and outbursts of anger. You can also become excessively controlling, which leads to more frustration fear, and anger. In the extreme, you can forget the sensitivities of others and can easily offend. As the imbalance becomes more acute, you can bring the job home with you and become excessively demanding and intolerant of those you love. Conflicts arise at work and at home. Just as your temperament becomes hotter, your face becomes increasingly inflamed, flushed, hot, and red. Your need to relax can easily lead you to indulge in excesses of sweets, alcohol, or television, which can actually feed the tension and result in more conflict.

Whenever an imbalanced choleric nature arises, it's time to relax, back up, and exhale. There's more to life than work and accomplishment. Besides, an imbalanced choleric temperament tends to waste a lot of energy in emotion and flare-ups. You become an impediment to your progress rather than a catalyst for forward movement. In the end, a person whose choleric nature takes over gets less done than do people who are able to relax and stay focused on the task at hand.

When you find your choleric temperament out of control, take a warm lavender bath. Lavender cools and relaxes the body. It reduces tension and inflammation. As the tension dissipates, circulation improves. Soon you will find your emotional life softening and your perspective opening up. New and creative solutions will emerge.

In addition to the lavender bath, take a gentle walk at lunchtime as well as after work. Don't power walk—always the symptom of an imbalanced choleric—but stroll. Spend time in nature, feeling its nourishing rhythms and returning to the stillness inside you. Get a massage, listen to soft music, and talk about your inner conflicts and frustrations with someone who loves and supports you.

Meanwhile, increase your consumption of cooked vegetables, avoid spicy foods, and reduce or eliminate alcohol. Soon you'll be back in balance, enjoying all the positive aspects of the choleric nature.

Sanguine Temperament: All Is Groovy

The sanguine temperament is characterized by optimism, humor, and a generally upbeat nature. You're positive, happy, and bent on enjoying life. Little or nothing gets you down. There's a spring in your step and a song in your heart. You tend to say just the right thing at the right moment. You've got plenty of emotional surplus, which makes you generous, understanding, and tolerant. At a party, you are the bon vivant.

All of this can have an extremely positive effect on your appearance. In the sanguine temperament, you often glow. Your attractiveness is at an all-time high. You are your most beautiful self. Your movements tend to be light and graceful, your words gentle and witty. What people see on the outside is what you are experiencing on the inside. How could there be a downside to this beautiful temperament?

Sanguines can actually carry the good life a little too far, partly due to intense curiosity. You want to study everything. Life thoroughly fascinates you, and every subject seems to draw your attention. Consequently, it's hard to focus and stay grounded. It's as if life has given you wings and all you can do is fly from one subject to the next, like a bee pollinating flowers. The more the sanguine nature becomes imbalanced, the less committed you are to any single endeavor or any individual person. You have trouble getting things done. You can't concentrate, discipline yourself, or work hard. You become impractical, flighty, and—like the element with which this temperament is associated—a little too airy. You party too much, work too little, and make mistakes too easily. There's little depth in your emotional life and virtually no real understanding of life's real demands.

When the sanguine pole is out of balance, it's time to get real. The place to start is with a spruce bath. Spruce has a dense, resinous aroma that grounds the senses and restores our intimate connection with our body and nervous system. Spruce strengthens our roots, our connection to the earth. It keeps our feet on the ground. It awakens and restores our practical nature.

In addition to the spruce bath, try vigorous physical exercise. Walk daily, putting a little vim and vigor in your step. Feel your body. Breathe deeply and exhale. Come back to yourself and your senses. Get a massage. Let a skilled healer put you back in touch with your body.

Eat more cooked whole grains, such as brown rice, millet, and barley. Whole grains strengthen the nervous system and ground us. This is a good time to eat high-quality, biodynamic animal foods, such as fish, eggs, turkey, or chicken, all of which can put us back in touch with our power and help ground us on the earth. Avoid sugar, alcohol, and (needless to say) recreational drugs.

The Phlegmatic: Everything's in Order, and I Want to Keep It That Way!

The phlegmatic temperament gives you the ability to think things through, to envision the future, and to create a plan for the fulfillment of your goals. This is the part of you that loves order and finds safety in routine. Your phlegmatic character creates rhythm, consistency, and stability. It loves the predictable. When you're in this character type, you are stocking up for the winter and making sure the car is tuned up and the oil's been changed. You balance the books; you're careful with your resources; you're frugal. You want tranquillity. Consistency is happiness. Thus, you guard against the unexpected as if it were a thief in the night. You don't like ups and downs. You are wise, temperate, and cautious. You tend to keep life and all of its gadgetry simple. You're patient. You don't need quick results—in fact, you're suspicious of anything that makes big promises or offers overnight rewards. You're meditative and appreciative of subtle pleasures. You like the tried and true. Nothing fancy, please. People can count on you.

As wonderful as all of these qualities are, when you're out of balance they can form a kind of prison. Life becomes ponderous, predictable, and flat with no excitement and little joy. You can become dull and boring to the point where the routine seems to choke the life out of you. Nothing seems important nor particularly valuable. Life comes and goes. Even more insidious, you can get so wedded to your routine that you become paralyzed. Your stubborn attachment to routine can actually be a cover for a fear of anything that is new, exciting, or unpredictable.

In other words, it's time to wake up. A lemon bath provides a therapeutic awakening of the nervous system and the senses. Lemon captures the warmth and energy of the sun. It pierces and disperses the dense clouds of stagnation that occur when the phlegmatic is stuck in his or her routine. It lightens the mood and brings freshness and energy to a lethargic life condition.

In addition to the lemon bath, eat more warming spices, such as garlic, cumin, coriander, pepper, and roasted red pepper, all of which warm and awaken the heart. Minimize dairy products, which can reinforce the phlegmatic nature by creating stagnation. Listen to music that inspires you, lifts your spirit, and opens your heart. Let yourself remember old ambitions and dreams. Do something entirely different each day. Dance—ballroom, swing, tango, or rock and roll. Dancing is that rare combination of rhythm and excitement, consistency and aliveness in movement. Take up a new hobby, such as tennis, golf, or billiards. Plan a trip to an exotic location that you've never visited but always wanted to see. In short, break out of your routine.

The Melancholic Temperament:
He Ain't Heavy, He's My Brother

When you are in the melancholic nature, you are caring, compassionate, and openhearted. You think about life less from the practical perspective than from the philosophical. You are spiritually oriented. You see the big picture and the great sweep of history. Yet you connect to individuals, especially to their pain. You listen attentively to people who want to share their tale of woe.

In the melancholic pole of your nature, you are introverted and extremely sensitive. You feel your own emotions intensely and can become preoccupied with your own emotional distress. You are often intuitive and highly perceptive about life, people, and people's histories. Your intellect is highly charged. You're often filled with philosophical or psychological insight—yet you are less interested in the future than the past. You want to understand yourself and how you got to where you are today. You struggle to connect the dots. You are preoccupied with the inner world but largely detached—at least in practical ways—from the outer one. You are more involved in your interior life than in changing the bigger world around you.

In the melancholic character, you can be extremely moody, moving from elation to depression within minutes. You also tend to worry a lot, especially about your physical health. When the melancholic nature takes over, you can easily become a hypochondriac. Melancholics wallow in deep existential questions, often finding pleasure in worry and dread. Eventually, the negative thinking associated with this temperament gets the better of you. It can cause physical distress, depression, and a wide array of physical ailments. This occurs largely because your life force has moved up into the head and drained the etheric body of its vital energies, thus causing the physical body to suffer. You become increasingly introverted. As this occurs, you experience less and less of your natural effectiveness and power.

If the melancholic nature has gotten the better of you, it's time to get out of your head and back into your body. Start with a series of rosemary baths, which will warm your body, awaken your senses, and dramatically boost your circulation. Rosemary revitalizes the body and lights the fire of our physical powers and passion. It puts us back in touch with the choleric nature and its inherent tendency to action and adventure. Also, try soaking your feet in spruce bath oils, which will ground you as well.

In addition to the rosemary baths and spruce foot soaks, eat cooked whole grains and root vegetables daily. Avoid raw vegetables and raw fruit, both of which cool the body and send the life forces upward. Keep your body warm, especially your feet (in winter, wear extra socks).

The Four Temperaments is a wonderful tool for self-analysis and self-healing. You can use it to understand your imbalances and to know what you can do to relieve stress and get back in step with your inner rhythms.

Rhythm is one of the great powers available to us if we learn how to experience it and use it for our own benefit. Follow your rhythms all the way to your most authentic and rewarding experience of beauty.

overall health of both children and adults. The hormones alone are believed to affect the growth and development of children. Many scientists now believe these same food-based steroids also play a role in the proliferation of breast, ovarian, and prostate cancers.

This same synthetic approach is applied to most skin care products. Most of us are applying a collection of chemicals and petroleum products to our faces. These may confer a small, short-term benefit, but they actually have long-term consequences. Many people are sensitive to these synthetic chemicals, and others are allergic to them. Rather than stem the aging process, some of these chemicals accelerate it. For example, parabens, the most widely used preservatives in skin care and cosmetics products, have a hormonelike effect on the skin and trigger inflammation, causing heat and swelling inside the tissues of your face. Inflammation shrinks the collagen fibers, the strands of protein that make your skin elastic, resulting in wrinkling and more rapid aging.

The effects of our modern farming, diet, and skin care are devastating. Skin problems abound, including premature aging, discoloration, acne, rosacea, and skin cancers. Obesity, digestive disorders, and a plethora of degenerative diseases are all on the rise.

You have the power to live in a more whole and healthful way. No matter who you are, you can reverse this alarming trend. Health and beauty are your birthright. You can take steps today to improve both. The place to start is with rhythm, as discussed in the previous chapter. The next essential step is to eat high-quality plant foods grown in rich, nonpolluted soil, meaning produce grown by biodynamic or, at the very least, organic methods. This same principle must be applied to your skin care products.

Quality and purity are the most important guidelines in choosing your foods as well as the substances you apply to your face and body. To make full use of these two lifesaving guides, we must understand exactly what they are and why they are so important.

Small-scale farming allows for hands-on care and attention to natural rhythms.

What Does Soil Have to Do with Beauty?

From the soil, health and beauty are born. The soil contains all the vital minerals, such as calcium, magnesium, and iron, that we need to live. But we can't eat the soil, so we've got to have a middleman, so to speak, a medium that supplies us with the earth's nutrients. The middlemen are plants. They absorb nutrients from the earth and make them available to us in the form of delicious foods. The calcium, phosphorus, and other minerals animal foods provide come from plants as well. In addition, plants create other essential substances, such as vitamins, that we need to live and be beautiful. In a great many cases, plants are the only source of substances that are essential for health and beauty.

The quality of the soil determines the quality of the plants grown in it. Soil that is rich in minerals gives rise to mineral-rich plants. Unfortunately, the more poisons in the soil, the more poisons in the plants grown in it and, hence, in the entire food chain.

Soil is a living, breathing life-form. Half a teaspoon of soil contains millions of bacteria and other microscopic organisms. And as every gardener knows, healthy soil also contains lots of worms, which aerate the soil and provide it with oxygen. All of these animals are busy consuming and digesting decayed plants to create a rich black earth called *humus,* which is the principle constituent of topsoil.

Humus contains nutrients, among them nitrogen, phosphorus, and potassium, which are needed to grow plants. Without a nutrient-rich humus, the soil is an infertile desert that cannot grow anything.

At the start of the twentieth century, farmers began adding synthetic fertilizers, pesticides, and herbicides to the soil as a way of creating more abundant crop yields. Unfortunately, these methods depleted the topsoil and

In biodynamic agriculture, soil is regarded as a living, breathing life-form.

What Is a Natural and Organic Food or Product?

Ever since the terms *natural* and *organic* were introduced to the marketplace, they have been a source of controversy. Many attempts have been made to define a natural or organic food or a natural skin care product; most resulted in more confusion than clarity. One of the best definitions to emerge came from an association of German manufacturers of drugs, supplements, cosmetics, and personal care products known as the BDIH. These guidelines, in fact, can be applied by anyone, anywhere, to discern if a food or skin care product can be considered "natural."

Here are the criteria you can use when looking for natural foods and skin care products.

- All raw materials are derived from nature.

- They are grown using organic and biodynamic methods.

- They have undergone only minimal processing.

- They are free of synthetic fragrances, colors, and dyes.

continued opposite

Choosing Foods: Quality First

I don't believe in dieting per se. I believe, fundamentally, that you are designed to be healthy and beautiful. It's in your nature—or, to be more precise, it's in your rhythms. The more you live within your rhythms, the more your inner wisdom will guide you to the right food choices and a diet that will lead to health and beauty.

The following guidelines will speed the recovery of both your health and beauty. The first and most important guide to choosing foods is quality. Quality means purity, to be sure, but it also means sustainability. The highest-quality foods—those produced by biodynamic methods—will not only restore your health and beauty, they will also restore the health and beauty of the earth. When you cannot obtain biodynamic foods, I urge you to choose organically grown foods. Anything short of these two will act as a drag on your health and beauty.

Once you have your quality standards in place, choose unprocessed plant foods as the majority of your daily diet. These include whole grains, fresh vegetables, beans, and fruits. Supplement your plant foods with smaller quantities of low-fat animal products, such as fish, low-fat dairy products, eggs, and low-fat meats. We should eat these foods as the Chinese and Mediterranean peoples do—in small quantities, and often as side dishes. This will provide you with all the protein your body needs. If you feel you need more, add more. Finally, allow yourself a small amount of the processed foods you enjoy as a treat. Do not eat these foods every day, but rather once a week, or two or three times a month. The less the better, especially if you want to lose weight. They should be the exception to your everyday diet.

Processed foods are the greatest source of calories in the food supply today and the primary reason we are suffering from an epidemic of overweight and obesity. Processed foods originate with a natural food, such as wheat, corn, potatoes, or sugar beets. During processing, the water, fiber, and many of the nutrients are removed from the natural foods, thus concentrating an enormous number of calories into a much smaller volume of food. A pound of corn, for example, provides only 390 calories, but a pound of corn chips contains 2,450 calories. A pound of cornflakes gives you 1,770 calories. Good old-fashioned popcorn, without butter, gives you 1,730 calories per pound. Add fat in the form of oil or butter and you get at least 2,270 calories per pound.

Natural foods are low in calories and rich in nutrients. As long as you eat mostly natural foods, your diet will naturally cause you to lose weight if you are overweight, or help you maintain a healthy weight.

How to Lose Weight Easily and Feel Satisfied

If you are concerned about losing weight, try to avoid calorically dense foods. A calorie, of course, is the unit by which we measure the energy content of foods. Lots of calories mean lots of potential energy. But if you don't burn all the calories you eat in your daily activities and exercise routine, the excess calories you consume are stored on your body as fat. Processed foods contain so many calories that you cannot possibly burn all the calories they give you. This means they are converted to fat.

In his book *The Pritikin Principle: The Calorie Density Solution,* Robert Pritikin shows how food manufacturers take a great quantity of natural foods, such as potatoes, and turn them into a small volume of processed foods, such as potato chips, all the while concentrating the calories in those chips. A pound of potatoes, for example, provides about 490 calories, Pritikin points out. But a pound of potato chips provides 2,400 calories. How is that possible? Food manufacturers take a lot of potatoes—far more than you could eat in a single sitting—and boil them, chop them, remove all the fiber and water, and then fry them in fat. The result is a relatively small volume of chips containing most of the calories from the original volume of potatoes, plus the calories picked up from the fat. Thus, a big bag of potatoes turns into a 1-pound bag of potato chips—with 2,400 calories.

The short list below will show you that natural plant foods, such as broccoli, carrots, apples, and oatmeal, contain relatively low amounts of calories. Compare these natural foods to the processed ones on the following list. The difference is huge.

- They contain no petroleum-derived synthetics (parabens, propylene glycol, silicones).

- They underwent exclusively nontoxic processing methods, and no synthetic substances (such as PEGs and sodium laureth sulfate) were used to process the ingredients.

- They have not been treated with any form of radiation at any stage of production.

- All efforts were made to ensure the product contains no genetically modified organisms (GMOs).

- The businesses that produce these substances use ecologically friendly harvesting and processing methods.

- No animals were used to test the product or in its production.

- The company producing the substance uses socially responsible business practices.

- The company uses recyclable and biodegradable packaging.

Unprocessed, Whole Plant Foods	Calories per Pound
Apples	270
Black beans, cooked	600
Brown rice, boiled	500
Kale	130
Oatmeal	280
Pasta	560
Potato, baked	490
Spinach	100
Strawberries	140
Yam, baked	525

© Pritikin Longevity Center, used by permission.

Plants That Heal Your Skin and Your Beauty

As we eat foods that restore our health and beauty, we must turn to high-quality skin care products for this same effect. The plants used for these products should be grown biodynamically or, at the very least, organically.

Special medicinal plants can work miracles for your skin. They are powerful sources of healing that people have been using to restore beauty for thousands of years. Here are some of the most effective plants for your skin. They can be found in many skin care products and salves. Apply these plant substances to your face and body, and watch your skin be transformed. Chapters 4 and 5 offer recipes for preparing skin care products of your own that include many of these healing and medicinal plants.

Anthyllis *Anthyllis vulneraria L*
(A member of the pea family. Also known as kidney wretch.)

Anthyllis produces a yellow to orange flower between April and June. It flourishes in clover fields and unfertilized stretches of land, usually by the side of the road, where only the strongest plants survive. All of this reveals anthyllis's strong life force, or vegetative power, in which traditional healers saw powerful restorative properties.

Anthyllis appears to promote urinary and kidney health. Traditional herbalists in Europe used anthyllis to heal wounds and treat skin disorders of all types, including acne, rosacea, dermatitis, and skin rashes.

Bryophyllum *Kalanchoe daigremontiana*
Family: Crassulaceae

Often referred to as *mother of thousands,* bryophyllum is a succulent water-bearing plant that along its leaves contains dozens of tiny versions of itself, like a mother carrying her young. These shoots fall from the mother plant, become embedded in the earth, and grow independently. Thus, wherever you find one bryophyllum, you're likely to find the rest of its family nearby.

Bryophyllum holds water and thrives in dry climates.

Bryophyllum is an excellent moisturizer. It rejuvenates the skin while stimulating it to retain its own moisture. It also contains many healing chemicals, including calcium and flavonoids. It is highly anti-inflammatory and immune boosting, and promotes wound healing. As it moisturizes, it also heals and restores the skin's flexibility, durability, and firmness.

Calendula (Marigold) *Calendula Officinalis L*

Family: Compositae/ Asteraceae

Calendula, whose beautiful yellow-orange flower blooms between April and June, is one of the most widely used and effective medicinal plants. Ancient healers discovered this remarkable botanical when they recognized that it bloomed each day at approximately 9 A.M. and closed around 3 P.M., with the rising and setting of the sun. This immediately suggested that calendula could absorb and retain the potent healing energies of the sun.

Calendula is loaded with powerful healing substances, including essential oils, saponins, carotenoids, bitter compounds, and flavonoids. It has been used throughout Europe to heal wounds, reduce inflammation, and treat bruises, burns, cuts, and skin ulcers.

Calendula regulates the skin's metabolism and promotes blood circulation. In skin care, it has been used to treat acne, eczema, rosacea, and skin that has been injured or inflamed or irritated.

German Chamomile *Matricaria Recutita*

Family: Compositae

Chamomile is another widely used herb. Its bloom is a little white flower with a yellow center. The flower is the part of the plant used for medicinal purposes. When applied to the skin, chamomile relaxes muscles, connective tissues, and the skin itself. It also relieves muscle spasms. When consumed internally, it relieves anxiety, headaches, nervous tension, and cramps.

Chamomile is an immune booster and is frequently used in tea form to treat cold and flu symptoms. It also enhances liver and digestive function. Chamomile tea combined with two slices of ginger can relieve painful menstrual and digestive cramps. Chamomile is a common herb in skin care products and healing salves, and it is widely available in tea leaf form.

Lavender *Lavendula officinalis, Lavendula augustifolia, Lavendula vera*

Family: Labiatae

Lavender is a woody shrub with beautiful blue and violet flowers that grow upward in tight swirls that look a little like cones. It originated in the Mediterranean region and now is grown in Europe and the United States, among other countries.

Lavender is one of the most effective and widely used herbs in skin care and healing. It is an anti-inflammatory, an antispasmodic, and an antiseptic. You can apply the essential oil directly to the skin, especially over aching or tense muscles, painful spasms, and aching joints. It is deeply relaxing while at the same time uplifting and inspiring. Lavender has a similar effect in baths.

The essential oil of lavender is helpful in treating acne, dermatitis, rosacea, oily skin, and dry skin. It balances the skin and stimulates cellular renewal and healing. In aromatherapy, lavender relaxes and soothes the troubled heart and mind.

Chapter 3

The Skin

No organ reveals your physical beauty more than your skin. You may pride yourself on the shine in your hair or the color of your eyes, but no other feature gives you a greater experience of your beauty. All of us, at one time or another, have felt blessed by the beauty that can suddenly arise from our skin. We have also cringed when our skin inexplicably breaks out in a rash or blemishes. The skin is the part of us on which we are most commonly judged; it is also the part we most commonly examine to judge ourselves.

The skin performs a multitude of tasks, most of which go unnoticed and unappreciated. It protects us from disease and the daily onslaught of particles large and small. It cools us when we are hot and warms us when we are cold. It heals wounds inflicted on it, often without any assistance from us. It absorbs sunlight to produce vitamin D, essential to the health of our bones and teeth, keeps itself moist, slows its own aging, and, every day, attempts to renew and restore its beauty.

While skin accomplishes all of this on its own, it still needs help. With every blemish, rash, and wrinkle, the skin is asking us to understand its nature and to support its efforts at self-renewal. Unfortunately, many of us respond to changes in our skin with practices that, in fact, assault and injure it further, consequently accelerating the aging process. On the other hand, many of us do nothing at all for our skin—but nonetheless expect it to remain clear, beautiful, and young.

In order to create the most effective program for our skin, we must begin by understanding what it does each day and how best to support its work.

The Dermis

The dermis might be thought of as a watery world. Living inside that world are blood and lymph vessels, small muscles, and nerves that convey our sense of touch. Also embedded in the dermis are sweat glands, hair follicles, and sebaceous glands, which produce sebum. The body is constantly resupplying the dermis with water to keep it moist, healthy, and beautiful.

Traversing the dermis are fibrous strands, about 80 percent of which are made of a protein called *collagen.* Collagen forms a dense matrix that protects the skin from splitting when it is pulled or twisted. The remainder of the strands are *elastin,* another protein-based fiber. Elastin acts like rubber bands; whenever the skin is pulled or stretched, elastin snaps it back into its original shape. As we age, however, the elastin weakens.

In youth, collagen and elastin are moist and plump, which makes the skin appear full, soft, and unlined. They give the skin its fullness and shape. As we age, the fibers are attacked by oxygen-free radicals, which causes them to dry, shrink, and cross-link with other collagen strands, forming structures that look like fishnetting. As the collagen base shrinks, the skin at the surface folds over on itself, forming wrinkles. Sometimes the collagen becomes so cross-linked that the skin itself looks like fishnetting. As discussed in chapter 2, the antidote to the problem of free radicals is the antioxidants found in plants. By eating antioxidant-rich plants and applying plant-based substances directly on your skin, you infuse the skin with antioxidants. These substances neutralize free radicals and slow the skin's aging process. Medicinal plants can heal the skin and restore much of its beauty and radiance.

The dermis is infused with blood vessels that bring oxygen and nutrition to nerves, glands, hair follicles, and cells, including those at the surface. When the body is cold, blood starts to move rapidly to bring in more warmth. When the body is hot, sweat glands start pumping moisture to the surface, where it evaporates and takes away some of the excess heat.

Also within the watery dermis lie waste products that are constantly being expelled from your cells and tissues. Those toxins are eliminated from your body by your lymph system. This is a complex network of vessels and nodes that absorbs intracellular waste particles from the gel-like fluid and takes it away to be neutralized by the liver and expelled by the kidneys. Within the lymph vessels and nodes are antibodies and immune cells, called *lymphocytes,* which destroy disease-causing agents.

Like any waste-removal system, the lymph works best when it is moving. When it is congested or blocked, waste builds up in the tissues and can cause blemishes, rashes, and irritations on the skin. Unlike the circulatory system, the lymph has no heart to help keep it moving. That job is left to you. You help keep your lymph circulating by moving your body, especially with exercise—walking, dancing, stretching, and yoga, for example. Needless to say, the better your lymph system is at removing toxic substances, the clearer and more beautiful your skin is.

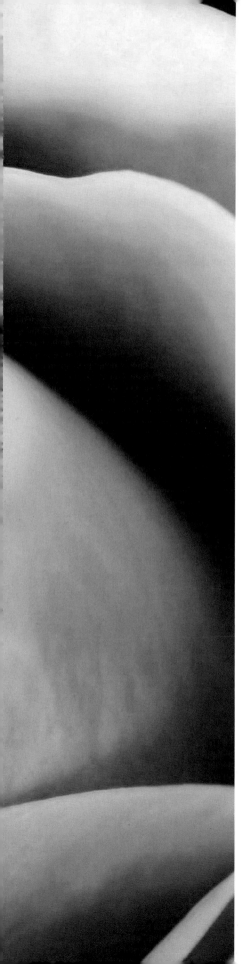

One way to reduce the burden on both your lymph and your skin is to reduce the toxic substances you ingest, especially through your diet. Try to avoid excess consumption of artificial substances, alcohol, animal fats, and cholesterol. Another way to keep your skin clear and the lymph unburdened is to stop smoking.

Deep within the dermis and down into the subcutaneous layer are hair follicles. The hairs that grow out of these follicles act like reeds in a pond. In the same neighborhood as the follicles are the sebaceous glands, which produce sebum. Along with the skin's water content, sebum moisturizes the skin. Once secreted, the sebum attaches itself to hairs and climbs upward to the surface along them to create the skin's soft yet protective acid mantle.

When the sebaceous glands are overactive, sebum can collect in the openings, or pores, of the skin, and in the places where the hairs appear at the surface. When this happens, pores and follicles can become blocked, infected, and inflamed, causing blemishes, boils, swelling, and scarring.

Also buried within the dermis are the sweat glands, which release moisture to cool the body. Sweat glands also eliminate waste, thus functioning as an adjunct to the kidneys and urinary tract.

The Subcutaneous Layer

Below the dermis is the subcutaneous layer, which contains fat, muscle, and some blood circulation. The fat and muscle act as a shock absorber for the skin, much as collagen does. At this layer, we find those annoying bands of cellulite, which is essentially fat, held in place by connective tissue lined with fat. Metabolic activities also take place here.

Ideally, diet and exercise habits promote both general health and the health and beauty of your skin. This thinking is the basis for a new approach to health care known as *salutogenesis,* or the act of promoting continual good health, as opposed to preventing or treating disease. A salutogenetic approach to skin care means using a health-promoting diet, lifestyle, and healing plants to help the skin perform its most basic and essential tasks.

Modern life has fostered a fragmented way of thinking that encourages us to see the parts of the body as separate from the organism as a whole. For example, there's no end to the number of beauty experts who will tell you how to have a beautiful face and clear skin but never mention the importance of the overall health of your body. Your commitment to being beautiful is really a commitment to your overall good health and vitality. Clear, radiant skin reflects good health. What most beauty experts won't tell you is that a beautiful face and radiant skin depend especially on the health of your kidneys and large and small intestines.

Chapter 4

The Face

I believe that virtually all people can have an attractive and, on many days of the week, even a beautiful face. To be more specific, virtually everyone can have more beautiful facial skin, even those who have had problems with acne, rosacea, and even minor scarring. Everyone's face can radiate a certain soft illumination that we all intuitively recognize as an essential part of beauty. Everyone can present a face that reflects confidence, self-love, and inner harmony.

The question is, how? All of us who want to be more beautiful ask ourselves these questions: First, what creates facial beauty, and second, what practical steps can we take to enhance, amplify, and restore it?

Facial beauty is more complex than the beauty of, say, hands, hair, or feet. This is partly because your face expresses the music of your inner life. No other part of the body so directly reveals your thoughts, emotions, internal conflicts, and long-term psychological patterns. The emotions that dominate your inner self show up on your face. Anger or depression, for example, show on your face. Conversely, if you are emotionally balanced and essentially happy, that, too, shows up on your face. More subtle feelings are communicated on the face, as well. Conceit and rejection of others, or of oneself, give the face a certain cast. Seriousness, playfulness, self-confidence, compassion—all of these are etched on the face. They, too, can determine whether you are perceived as beautiful.

Holistic Versus Conventional Skin Care

Many, if not most, conventional skin care products are developed in response to the belief that your skin is misbehaving and therefore must be managed or even coerced into acting properly. In essence, the skin is a recalcitrant child and often even the enemy. Drugs and other forms of medicine are needed to force the body to function properly and the skin to look healthy. However, as you know, the more extreme the medicine, the greater the side effects. Very often, harsh skin care products cause us to exchange one set of problems for another.

Holistic skin care sees the body as an integrated unit in which every function works together to achieve the harmony that is health. One of the consequences of health is beautiful skin. Rather than seeing the body as the enemy, the holistic approach views the body as a wise friend who must be understood and supported. We must learn from the body and act in harmony with its basic behaviors and laws.

A healing diet, competent digestion, regular exercise, and a commitment to achieving emotional harmony all combine to create glowing skin and a beautiful face. On the other hand, the more out of balance our lives are in any of these areas, the more our skin suffers and the more we depend on conventional products and potions.

A good illustration of the very different types of thinking that underlie the conventional versus the holistic approaches to skin care is AHAs, or alpha hydroxy acids.

Alpha hydroxy acids (AHAs) were originally derived from the acids in plants and milk products. Today, virtually all of the AHAs on the market are synthetically produced and are far more powerful than their natural predecessors. AHAs have different effects on the skin depending on the concentration. At concentrations of 3 percent or lower, AHAs bind with water and hold it to the surface of the skin, thus acting as a moisturizer. At concentrations of 4 percent or more, AHAs break down the adhesive substance that holds cells in place within the stratum corneum and cause these dead cells to slough off, exposing the living cells below. The living cells look younger and brighter, which is part of the reason AHAs have become so popular. Unfortunately, synthetic AHAs often injure the stratum corneum and the acid mantle, leaving the skin unprotected and vulnerable to environmental assault. Moreover, without a strong stratum corneum, the skin loses moisture and ages more quickly. This usually results in a dependence on moisturizers and other products—but these products can never compensate for the moisture loss and consequent aging that occur when the skin is injured. Strong AHAs can also irritate mucous membranes.

AHAs have, however, been shown to be effective in the treatment of light-damaged skin, and some reports claim they can help people suffering from thickening of the skin caused by hyperkeratinization (excess production of keratinocytes). AHAs do have their place, but only when they are used in a balanced way and as part of a holistic approach to skin care.

Concentration is the all-important factor. Natural products, derived from medicinal plants, fruits, and milk products, possess AHAs in safe and appropriate concentrations at which the AHAs serve as good moisturizers or mild exfoliants. The cells that are exfoliated are most likely those that were ready to slough off from the stratum corneum. The stratum corneum and the acid mantle are left intact. Synthetic AHAs tend to be more concentrated and therefore more injurious to the skin.

This is just one of the many reasons to avoid synthetic products. They often have severe side effects and tend to do more harm than good. This rule should be followed strictly with respect to facial products. Plant-based skin care products contain an abundance of antioxidants and other plant compounds that reduce oxidation and inflammation, the two processes that age the skin. As I discussed in chapter 2, many plant substances heal the skin. Plus, plants contain that indefinable etheric or life energy, or what the Chinese call *chi*. Chi arises from overall health and from healthy skin. It is also enhanced by the chi in living substances that you apply to your face.

The second rule is to touch your face with gentle, loving care. Don't scrub your face or treat it harshly. Your face is the physical manifestation of your inner life. When you treat your face with healing love, gentleness, and compassion, you are treating your inner life in the same way. You are actually healing your own heart when you care for your face with love. And in a very short time it shows. Soon, the care and love you give your face spreads to other aspects of your life.

Here is a short exercise to illustrate my point. Close your eyes and gently place your hands on your face. Take a deep breath, exhale, and release as much tension from your face and body as you can. Feel the intimacy you suddenly have with yourself. Now, very gently, with the tips of your fingers, massage your forehead. Do this with great care, running your fingertips across your eyebrows and then down along the orbital bones around your eyes. Move to your cheekbones, massaging gently and lovingly. Feel your facial muscles start to relax and let go of tension. Move your fingertips along the bridge of your nose, to the nose itself, and then to your upper lip. With a very light touch, massage your lips and the muscles around your mouth. Feel every facet of your face. As you massage your face, notice how other areas of your body, especially your lower back and pelvis, let go of tension. Move your fingertips to your cheeks and very lightly massage them in a clockwise fashion. Move your hands to the back of your jawbone, right beneath your ears, and gently massage the jawline from the back to the chin. As you massage your face, notice that your hands and fingertips are filling with life energy that is then conferred to your face. Continue to breathe. Move your hands down to below your chin and massage below your neckline, gently pulling the flesh of your lower chin toward your neck. Massage the sides and back of your neck, paying particular attention to the area at the back of your head, where your skull and spine join. Place your hands back over your face and take a moment in the silence. Relax. Take your hands away from your face and open your eyes. Notice how you feel. Aren't you more connected with yourself? Don't you feel a little more relaxed, a little more soothed, and a little more comforted? Your face can be a gateway to your heart. Treat your face with loving-kindness, and you will encourage the healing of your heart.

The third type, mineral oil–based moisturizers, is derived from petroleum. These moisturizers are heavy and tend to clog the pores and block elimination. Further, they are difficult to remove from the skin without heavy soap. They also trap heat from the sun and atmosphere and raise the temperature of the skin, resulting in inflammation. People with sensitive skin often react negatively to mineral oils and suffer blemishes and acne.

The last group is vitamin E–oil moisturizers, also known as *tocopherols*. Vitamin E is an antioxidant that neutralizes free radicals, protects skin cells, and slows the aging process. Vitamin E tocopherol oils are derived from a variety of plants, most often alfalfa, almond oil, fennel, and wheat germ. They can also be produced synthetically, but you should avoid the synthetic version, because it very likely will not have the same degree of potency nor protective effects. If you use vitamin E oil, make sure it's from plant sources, such as wheat germ oil, as opposed to a synthetic version.

Some common moisturizers do not use any oils. These are called *humectants*. They can draw moisture to your skin from the environment, but the effect can also backfire and draw moisture from the dermal layer of your skin. People with acne tend to react better to humectants than to oils.

Always choose organic or biodynamic plant-based products. In addition, use any of the moisturizing masks described below, each of which can be applied in the evening and rinsed away before bed. These masks contain antioxidants and phytochemicals that not only hydrate but also purify the skin. They are also easy to make.

Alternatively, the Dr. Hauschka approach to daytime moisturizing is to help the skin hold in moisture, support the skin's own moisture-producing activities, and heal the skin of blemishes or other disorders. Dr. Hauschka daytime moisturizers include:

are exhaustion, stress, excess consumption of spicy foods and alcohol, and changes in temperature and climate. Rosacea is among the most common manifestations of this type of sensitivity.

The second arises when the skin becomes flaky and itchy and develops spots of redness. Such a condition can emerge from emotional distress, changes in climate and temperature, and travel.

Aging skin is accelerated when we are overexposed to free radicals, which are caused primarily by cigarette smoking, exposure to sunlight, industrial and environmental pollutants, a diet rich in processed and animal foods, and prolonged stress.

Normal skin is a result of the skin's basic functions of self-moisturizing, healing, renewal, and cleansing working in a balanced and optimal way. Most people with normal skin also experience periods when one part of the skin is slightly oily while another part is dry. This is referred to as *combination skin*.

The skin, remarkably, is constantly healing itself. Given the right conditions—such as a healing diet, exercise, and healing external treatments—it can restore much of its beauty and inspiring glow. All the skin care recommendations provided address all five skin conditions. In fact, if you follow the dietary and skin care advice described in the preceding chapters, most skin disorders will clear up by themselves.

Nevertheless, some intractable conditions call for further care. The following homemade treatments use medicinal plants or herbs to treat acne and rosacea. Follow with homemade moisturizers to treat dry skin and homemade toners to treat oily and normal skin.

Alternatively, use a variety of Dr. Hauschka products for all five types of skin conditions.

A Healing Mask for Acne

Combine 1 teaspoon each of the following ingredients: honey, wheat germ, and goldenseal powder. Mix thoroughly and apply to your face for 10 minutes. Apply the mask twice a week.

Herbal Formula for Treating Rosacea

Cleanse your face with a homemade oatmeal soap.

Fill a quart-sized basin with water and add $1/2$ cup rolled or steel-cut oats. Mix gently until the water becomes cloudy. Allow 5 to 10 minutes for the oats to settle to the bottom of the basin. Gently and lovingly rinse your face with just the oatmeal water. Avoid applying the actual grain to your face. Use the press-and-roll motion described in chapter 4 to cleanse.

After cleansing, apply a homemade toner that contains any or all of the following herbs: goldenseal, yarrow, and chamomile. (Instructions for making the toner are described on page 75.)

Herbal Formula for Treating Acne

Virtually all traditional herbalists begin their treatment of acne by supporting and strengthening the blood-cleansing organs, especially the liver and kidneys. The process begins, of course, by eliminating foods that burden these organs, especially those that are processed or contain caffeine, sugar, artificial substances, pesticides, and high levels of fat.

The following herbal formula reduces the burden on blood-cleansing organs and supports the elimination of acne.

Combine 1 teaspoon each of the following dried herbs in 4 to 5 cups of water: burdock root, dandelion root, gingerroot, nettles herb, Oregon grape root, red root, and yellow dock. Boil for 10 minutes. Remove from the heat and allow the brew to steep for 10 minutes. Drink 1 cup twice a day for three days straight, and then abstain from the formula for three days. These six days are considered a single round. Repeat for three to four more rounds.

At the same time, use the recommended herbal cleansers, moisturizers, and toners, the toner preferably containing echinacea.

The first dimension is the material, or physical body, the part we can see. The second is the life force, or life energy—what the Chinese refer to as *chi* and what Steiner called the *etheric body.* Your life force is an integrated body of energy that infuses every cell, organ, and system of your body. The etheric energy body determines the vitality and youthfulness of your physical body. A strong etheric body causes your physical body to age more slowly and maintain its youth for a much longer period. The third aspect of your humanity is your emotional body, or what Steiner called the *astral aspect* of your being. This is the part that has distinct likes and dislikes; it reacts to your experiences and plays a central role in your decisions and behaviors. The fourth is your spirit. Steiner said that this spiritual aspect of your being understands your purpose for living. It also lives on after your physical body dies. Steiner maintained that, in the end, all of us are attempting to infuse the physical, etheric, and emotional planes with the spiritual dimension of our lives—a transformation that, among other things, brings about greater goodness, truth, and beauty.

The way to restore health and enhance your beauty, however, is to infuse your body with an abundance of life energy, Hauschka and Steiner said. This enhanced life energy elevates the function of all your organs and systems. It brings your emotions into balance and promotes feelings of confidence, well-being, and joy. It imbues your physical body with harmony and radiance that emerges as true beauty.

Dr. Hauschka dedicated his life to developing plant-based medicines that contain both the plant's active ingredients and its life energies. In the 1920s, he created

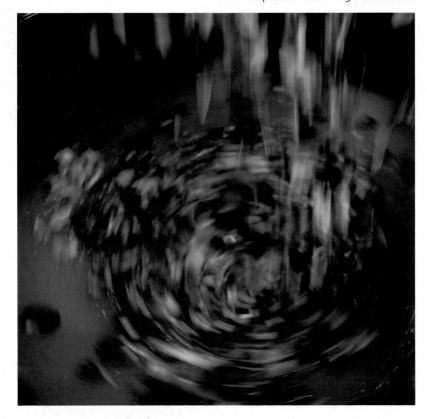

a seven-day rhythmical process in which he used the opposing forces of nature—light and darkness, coolness and warmth, motion and stillness—to coax forth the medicinal ingredients and vital energies from the plant so they could be administered to people. He and Elisabeth Sigmund brought this same approach to the Dr. Hauschka Skin Care Products.

In our own way, each of us is searching for ways to boost our life force and enjoy the fruits that such an experience brings. There are many ways to do that, and all of them contribute to making you healthier and more beautiful.

Dr. Hauschka's unique extraction methods preserve the vital energies of living plants.

Boosting Your Life Force for Health and Beauty

Everyone who touches you with caring, compassion, or love elevates your life energy and contributes to your health and beauty. The opposite is also true. Touching a person in anger or with selfishness weakens the life force. Your body can sense what's in the heart of the person whose touch it feels. Sometimes the body welcomes that touch—indeed, it can drink up the energy that passes from the person who offers a loving or healing touch. At other times, the body recoils from or armors itself against negative feelings implicit in a person's touch.

We all seek to be touched with love or caring because these are the mediums through which an abundance of life energy can pass between people. A loving or caring touch has the potential to raise our life energy, improve our health, and enhance our beauty.

All forms of skin and body care enhance your life force and boost your health and beauty—that is, when they are administered by someone who is loving, compassionate, and skilled. A facial given by such a person can transform you. So, too, can a therapeutic massage. The esthetician's or the healer's skill and compassion are transmitted from her hands into your skin and etheric body, making your etheric field stronger and more alive. The result is a dramatic change on every level of your being—your mood is softer and more balanced; your body is more in harmony and therefore healthier; and your appearance is more relaxed, open, and beautiful.

Rudolf Steiner described in great detail the energetic connection between people. Our thoughts, emotions, and words are bundles of etheric energy, Steiner said, that pass from one person to the next. That same etheric energy passes between people when they touch. The effects thoughts, emotions, words, and touch have on us depend on the type of emotion and intention they carry. For example, Steiner said that loving thoughts, intended to support other human beings, take a form similar to a flower. When you think loving or caring thoughts about another person, bundles of etheric energy leave your body and enter the field of the person for whom they are intended. There they enrich, strengthen, and brighten the person's etheric body, overall health, and beauty.

Each of us creates our reality on the basis of our thoughts, emotions, and actions. On the other hand, our inner realities are also created by the types of etheric energies to which we are exposed. This gives us a tremendous power to strengthen our health, improve our lives, and develop our beauty. We can do this simply by exposing ourselves to many sources of love, compassion, and care. All of the following practices do exactly that.

- Spend time in nature. A forest is packed with harmonious etheric energy. The ocean sends waves upon waves of beautiful life force to you. Nature literally bathes us in life energy, which is why we feel so different after we've

spent a little time by the sea or in a wood. The etheric waves are creating order, harmony, and beauty inside you. A thirty-minute walk in a park or a wood or by a river, a lake, or the sea has the power to transform your inner world and outer beauty.

Here's a little experiment you can do. Take a quiet half-hour walk with a friend by a lake, along the ocean, or in a forest. Before you take such a walk, take a good look at your friend's face. Notice the expression and the lines on her or his face. After the walk, again look closely at your friend's face. In the vast majority of cases, you will notice that your friend has relaxed. His or her face will be fuller, more alive, and less lined. He or she will look younger. The effect will not simply be in his or her appearance, however. You both will feel more vital, more alive, and more balanced emotionally. You have been profoundly changed by the harmony and beauty of nature and thus become more harmonious and beautiful yourself.

If possible, spend thirty minutes a week walking in nature.

- Eat unprocessed plant foods, especially fresh vegetables, fruits, and whole grains that have been grown biodynamically or organically. Fresh foods that have been grown in clean, pure soil retain their life energies even after harvest. Those life energies infuse your body when you eat these foods. Steiner said that we need the forces of all vital foods to develop a strong, healthy spiritual life.

- Express gratitude and love throughout the day, especially when you drink water or when you bathe or shower. Whenever you drink water, consider expressing love and gratitude silently into the water before you drink. Do the same when you bathe or shower.

  In chapter 1, I suggested you "potentize" your bath water by swirling the water in the shape of a figure 8. As you do this, express your gratitude for your beautiful body and your life. Express the love you have for your life, for yourself, and for those closest to you. These thoughts will enter the water and promote your health and beauty as you bathe.

- Dance or do rhythmic exercise. *Eurythmy,* a form of therapeutic dance based on Steiner's teachings, blends harmonious movements to strengthen your etheric body, overall health, and beauty. All forms of rhythmic dance, such as ballroom or tango, boost life energy. So, too, do rhythmic forms of exercise such as tai chi chuan, chi gong, yoga, and tennis.

- Seek out therapeutic massage and healing touch, including Reiki and massage practices founded on the ancient Chinese practice of acupuncture. Acupuncture is a 3,000-year-old healing art based on the perception that life energy flows through the physical body along distinct pathways, or meridians. Along these meridians lie hundreds of acupuncture points that when stimulated by the shallow insertion of a needle or by pressure

from the practitioner's fingers act as generators of life energy. Many scientists have used sensitive electronic equipment to demonstrate that these points do indeed trigger an electrical charge that runs along the meridian lines described by Chinese healers.

- Listen to beautiful, harmonious music. As everyone knows, music can change our life condition in seconds. Music, of course, is harmonious waves of energy that transform your physical, etheric, and emotional bodies, thus restoring inner balance and beauty to your life. Try to hear live music whenever possible. Local colleges and universities are good places to hear all kinds of music, from classical to jazz, folk, and rock and roll.

- Use skin care products made of pure plant substances, preferably grown biodynamically or organically.

- Practice rhythm. Your health and beauty depend on your capacity to create and sustain an orderly life.

All of these practices will strengthen your etheric energy, which in turn will support your physical, emotional, and spiritual health and beauty. Everything that supports your life force also promotes the health, youthfulness, and beauty of your skin. These life-supporting activities are therefore practical forms of skin care.

Still, aging is inevitable, which means we must become more and more conscious of exposing ourselves to the sources of healing and beauty. As we age, we must become wise. You don't need to know very much at twenty or twenty-five in order to look young and be beautiful. But when you start passing through your thirties, forties, and fifties, your health and beauty increasingly depend on the wisdom of your choices and how well you care for yourself.

There's a reason for that, Steiner said. During your mid-thirties, the life force turns its attention away from your physical body and toward your internal development, namely your wisdom and spiritual growth. The universe has a plan for you, Steiner said, and it is written into all four levels of your being. That plan unfolds in its own unique way so that you can become fulfilled and truly beautiful—that is, unless you fight it.

Embrace and Make the Most of the Stage of Life You Are In

Our culture is waging war against the natural and inevitable process of aging. In messages that are all too obvious, the culture draws a line in the sand, so to speak, and says that after the age of thirty-five, we are increasingly uninteresting and less and less beautiful. All that is good, true, and beautiful in our mature years is often dismissed or ignored. The consequence is that we know little about the aging process, and even less about the gifts that await us after the age of forty.

Every ancient and traditional culture has offered a kind of mythological blueprint for how humans develop, become their own unique selves, and fulfill their purpose for living. This blueprint was intended to reveal the challenges, rewards, and potential beauty in each stage of life. There are rewards and gifts to be earned and integrated at each phase of your maturity. Every one of those gifts is essential if you are to become whole and fulfilled.

Rudolf Steiner observed that human life unfolds in seven-year cycles. He maintained that in your mid-thirties, your life force makes a dramatic turn away from the physical body. At that point, it devotes itself increasingly to the job of developing your inner world and your spiritual life. As you age, less and less energy is dedicated to keeping young, while more and more is used to develop your growing wisdom and spiritual connection to the universe at large.

From ages 7 to 14 we have strong physical health and an abundance of energy.

Ages 0 to 7:
Coming into Life

The first seven years of life are a gradual development into individuality. The child's energetic, or etheric, body is still strongly linked to its mother, especially in the first few years. During these early years, it's impossible for the child to distinguish between herself and her mother.

Our conventional way of thinking is to picture us as growing up after birth, but Steiner maintained that we, in effect, "grow down." What he meant was that the etheric, emotional, and spiritual aspects of our nature gradually join with the physical body, and as they do, we develop individuality.

The first sign of that individuality is the development of mobility: crawling, and then walking. Slowly, we come to know more and more about what we want and need. We develop preferences and temperament. All of this suggests that more and more of who we truly are is grounded in physical form.

When the life force is sufficiently grounded in the body, the child's energetic body is strong enough to cause the teeth to burst forth, which gives him or her the ability to eat solid food. At about five years of age, the child goes off to school, and not long afterward, perhaps at six or seven, permanent teeth appear. We have gradually moved away from the mother and into greater and greater stages of individuality. We are now ready for the next phase of our maturity.

Ages 7 to 14:
Stronger Health and Healing Abilities

Between the ages of seven and fourteen, childhood illnesses can appear, such as measles, mumps, and chicken pox. This is the moment when the immune system must become strong in order to give us the defenses we need to survive. High fevers develop, the body fights for its health and life, and in the process, the immune system arises as a powerful ally that can ward off antagonists from the environment. At the same time, hormones change and the body rapidly matures.

In order for the immune system to meet the challenges of the environment, the etheric body must be fully grounded in the physical body. The body needs all of its energies to fight off illness. Therefore, it draws the life force to itself. The etheric body fully joins the physical body. Once the childhood diseases are overcome, the energy from the life force is used to fuel a rapid burst of hormonal and physical changes. We have strong physical health and an abundance of energy, and we're ready to enter the next big stage in life—puberty and the ability to procreate.

Quality Determines Quantity

The quality of a skin care product, or a food, determines its effects on your skin, health, and happiness. Most of our health problems today, especially obesity, come from two related sources. The first is the quality of our food. Too much of our food is poisoned with synthetic pesticides, fertilizers, hormones, antibiotics, and harmful bacteria. All of these substances combine in our bodies to trigger intense immune-system reactions and ongoing inflammation, both of which accelerate aging and lead to skin problems and major disease.

The second problem is that most of our food is processed, which, as discussed in chapter 2, indicates an overabundance of calories and artificial ingredients. A diet rich in processed food ultimately causes obesity and sickness. If the quality of our food is substantially improved, the result will be better nourishment, satisfaction, and beauty. If you are overweight, you will lose weight without trying.

I urge you to buy fresh, organic or biodynamic, antioxidant-rich whole grains, vegetables, and fruits, and to reduce as much as possible all processed foods as well as conventionally raised animal foods. I am not, however, going to ask you to deprive yourself of any of your favorite foods. On the contrary, if you are a lover of chocolate, for example, I recommend that you buy the highest quality, such as Repunzell chocolate, made from biodynamic ingredients. If you enjoy animal foods, I urge you to buy animal foods that have been raised organically or biodynamically.

You don't have to diet to improve your health, beauty, or weight. You just have to improve the quality of your food and then add regular gentle exercise.

Concerns About Price

People argue that cost is a factor when it comes to buying organic or biodynamic food. It's true that organic and biodynamic foods are often more expensive at the checkout counter, but if you purchase these high-quality foods, you will actually be more satisfied with your diet, have fewer cravings, eat less, and experience far greater health and beauty.

Consider a hidden cost in our food today: the cost of medical care. The more poisons you consume, the sicker you become and the greater your risk of major illness grows. The foods we eat are the primary reason we must make so many visits to the doctor and the hospital and why so many of us are dependent on pharmaceutical drugs. Those costs are enormous. The higher the quality of your food, the better your health, and the less dependent you will be on medical care, especially as you age.

Tips for Making Food Preparation Easier

To cut down on the time needed to prepare healthful and delicious meals, I recommend that you cook larger quantities on the weekend. Prepare a large pot of whole grains, another of soup, and still another of beans. These foods can be refrigerated and reheated during the week when you arrive home after a busy day.

Vegetables are health and beauty fast foods. You can boil or steam greens in less than seven minutes. Simply rinse the greens, put about an inch of water in the bottom of a pot, place the greens in a steamer, and the steamer in the pot. Cover and turn up the flame to medium-high. Steam for three to seven minutes, depending on the thickness of the greens, and you've made a high-fiber, high-antioxidant, high-phytochemical, low-calorie snack. Purchase organic sauces and dressings to enhance the flavor of your vegetables, if you like.

Make enough food every evening to have leftovers for lunch the following day. You can place the food in plastic containers and bring them to your office, or simply reheat them at home. You'll have a healthful and delicious lunch every day.

Soak grains the night before cooking them to make them more digestible and their nutrients easier to assimilate. If you prefer, you can add a teaspoon of apple cider vinegar to the soaking water to promote a fermenting process, which further aids digestion.

The recommendations that follow offer suggestions for seven days' worth of breakfast and dinner meals. Menu plans are also provided in chapter 9 for further planning. This shorter version of the menu plan will help you establish a healing diet and a natural rhythm through the week. Monday's breakfast, for example, includes the cooked whole grain quinoa; Tuesday's features oats. Monday's dinner includes cod; Tuesday's spinach salad. Many of us are at a loss when considering what to cook each night. On this program, you will know exactly what to prepare. As this rhythm becomes a habit, you will naturally make adjustments without having to think too much about what you'll be eating each day.

You may already have a good rhythm with your dinner meals. In that case, you may only want to substitute some of the ingredients to improve their quality. Of course, you can modify these suggestions any way you like. Try to make all your food choices organic or biodynamic.

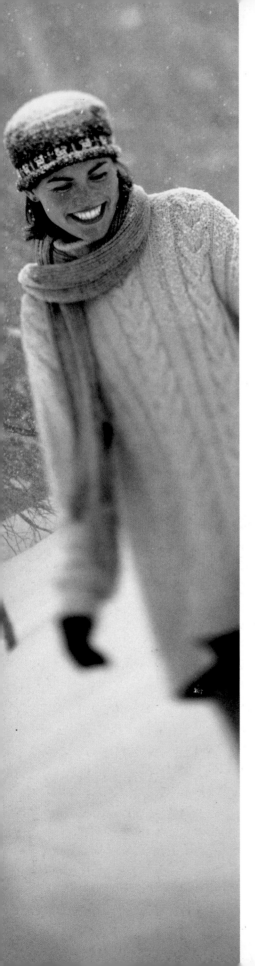

Body Oils

Protect your body skin for the day ahead by applying a high-quality body oil or body moisturizer, rich in plant essential oil, which will balance your skin and keep it warm and moist throughout the day. The finer body moisturizers contain essential oils from any of the following medicinal plants: lavender, rosemary, lemon, spruce, blackthorn, and arnica. Lavender, which calms, strengthens, and supports the nervous system, is recommended when you are under stress.

Toner

After drying your body, gently blot your face dry with a cotton towel and then apply a gentle toner, one made from organic or biodynamic extracts and essences. A good toner will prepare the skin for a daily moisturizer.

Moisturizer

Moisturizers should protect the skin but also encourage the skin's own moisturizing functions. Use a moisturizer made from the highest-quality healing plants. Among the ingredients you'll want in your moisturizer are essential oils of anthyllis, witch hazel, Saint-John's-wort, and calendula, and wheat germ, olive, and jojoba oils. A good moisturizer will balance dry, mature, and normal skin.

Moisturizers can be changed based on the seasons, as the weather makes different demands on your skin. In severe winter climates, you will need more protection. Good winter moisturizers often contain healing plants, such as marshmallow, avocado, Saint-John's-wort, rose petal, and rose hip. These protect the epidermis and soothe and heal skin irritated by harsh weather.

For spring and summer, a good moisturizer is one containing an array of healing herbs such as quince seed, marshmallow, and witch hazel. These soothe and heal but do not provide the same level of heavy protection that a winter moisturizer does.

Eye Care

Apply a fine eye cream made with castor oil, beeswax, and rosewax. Use it sparingly to protect the delicate tissue around the eyes. Use your eye cream in the morning, not at night, so your skin can breathe and heal while you sleep.

How Does Your Morning Care Feel?

Once you have cleansed, toned, and moisturized your face, feel your skin. It should feel relaxed, yet bright and alive. It should not be tight or in any way uncomfortable. Your skin care regimen should, in essence, be a healing program that results in even more beautiful skin. If your face feels tight or oily, or if blemishes arise, your skin is likely in rebellion against a product, or products, that contain synthetic ingredients. For the most beautiful skin, use products made of healing plants that were grown organically or biodynamically.

Step 3. Healing Breakfast

This seven-day menu plan, along with the menus and recipes in chapter 9, will help you establish a morning and evening meal rhythm that is easy to follow and maintain. I recommend that you simply repeat this menu four times, plus two days, for the full thirty-day program.

The morning meal comprises cooked whole grains. Each kind of grain has a distinctive, subtle flavor. All provide an array of essential and healing benefits, including vitamin E, protein, other vitamins, minerals, and fiber. Whole grains are energy foods. They are rich in complex carbohydrates, which are slowly absorbed and provide long-lasting energy throughout the day. They also promote healthy digestion. You will recall from chapter 3 that digestion is a key to healthy and beautiful skin. Cooked whole grains are a key to good digestion and elimination.

All of these grains require twenty-five minutes or less of cooking time. Remember that you have been soaking the morning grain from the previous night. Develop the habit of starting to soak the following day's grains while preparing today's breakfast. (For cooking instructions and ways to enhance the flavor of your breakfast grains, see chapter 9, "Menus and Recipes for Healthy and Beautiful Skin.")

Here is the morning menu:

Monday: Quinoa. Quinoa is regarded by nutritionists as a superfood for its protein, vitamin, and mineral content.

Tuesday: Oat Groats. Oat groats are a whole grain packed with nutrients. Prepared like a hot cereal, they have a warm, nutty flavor.

Wednesday: Seven-Grain Cereal. Seven-grain cereal is available in bulk at most natural foods stores. It provides a wide variety of grains, is rich in flavor, and is especially hearty in winter.

Thursday: Millet. Millet is a high-protein grain that's rich in nutrients and has a mild, delicious flavor.

Friday: Spelt. A high-protein grain, spelt is rich in flavor.

Saturday. Poached eggs on sprouted grain toast with smoked salmon (optional).

Sunday. Buckwheat pancakes topped with organic yogurt and maple syrup served with one or two organic breakfast sausage links or bacon, if desired.

Special Footbath

We can eliminate a great deal of stress and toxic emotion simply by caring for our feet.

On nights when you cannot take a full bath, try soaking your feet in an enamel bowl or a plastic tub filled with very warm water and a bath concentrate. If you are staying home that night, use essential oils of spruce, lavender, or sage, all of which relax and draw toxins and stagnant emotions from your tissues. If you are going out, use rosemary or lemon, which will leave your feet feeling like they are dancing on air.

Soak your feet for at least 10 minutes. Dry them off and brush them with a loofah or a natural-bristle body brush.

Gently massage into the tissues of your feet and nails a strengthening and healing essential oil such as neem, apricot kernel oil, lavender, or chamomile. Apply a moisturizer when you are finished.

As you give your feet all this love, get in touch with them. They take a pounding every day. Find the tender spots and gently massage them. If your feet are dry and cracked, apply a foot cream with healing herbs such as rosemary or goldenseal, rice starch, and silk to restore circulation and a healthy environment for the skin tissue.

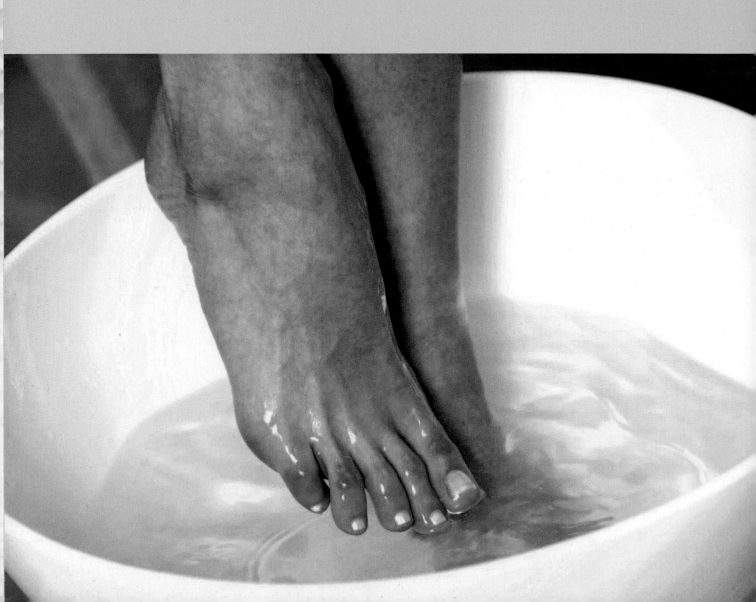

Detox Footbaths

This is a special footbath designed to remove physical and emotional toxins.

Soak your feet in a bowl of very warm water with 1 tablespoon ground mustard and 1 teaspoon cayenne pepper for 10 to 15 minutes. Add very warm water to the footbath occasionally to maintain the temperature. Once you are done, dry your feet and drink 8 ounces warm water with the juice of 1 lemon in it. The lemon drink is a traditional tonic for the liver. It also helps overcome constipation.

1. Do Nothing

If possible, set aside at least twenty minutes every weekend to do nothing. Just feel your feelings, experience your rhythms, and feel the beautiful rest that comes over you when you have nothing at all to do.

2. Get a Massage

If you can, get a massage on the weekend. Many massage schools offer reduced rates on weekends so that their students can practice and learn their craft. Call your local massage school and find out what it is offering.

If you can, get at least two massages every month. Try to schedule your massage on the same day of the week, and roughly the same time of the day, in order to establish a rhythm that will reinforce its healing effects.

3. Take a Long Walk

Take time for a long walk every weekend, if possible. As discussed in chapter 1, you need not power walk. Instead, start out at a comfortable pace, and as you progress, increase or decrease your speed depending on how your body is reacting. Speed is not as important as distance and time. Increase the distance and time you walk as your fitness improves—and if you walk regularly, your fitness *will* improve. Whenever possible, walk in nature—a forest, a beach, or a park. Most important of all, enjoy your walk.

As you are walking, notice nature. See its beauty. Feel how it is feeding you with love and gratitude. Find something on your path that strikes you as beautiful and bring it home. It's a gift from nature. Display it in a special place and notice it again and again throughout the week.

Each season, I create a nature table on which I place plants, crystals, a beautiful card, flowers, and art I've discovered on my walks. Recently, I got my florist to supply a few organic and biodynamic flowers, which I now purchase regularly. Many farmers' markets also sell organic flowers. All of these gifts from nature are an inspiration to me. I want them displayed prominently in my home because they remind me of the love that is constantly flowing from nature.

4. Care for Your Hair

A wonderful treatment for hair that's been damaged by chemical treatments, sun, wind, chlorine, or heat is to apply a hair lotion made of healing herbs, followed by healing essential oils. Here's how you can do it.

Apply a hair lotion that contains herbal extracts to your hair for five to ten minutes, massaging your scalp thoroughly. The extracts should include some of the following: neem, nettle, calendula, rosemary, and arnica. Begin exploring your scalp gently with

your fingertips in gentle, circular motions. You may find tender spots, especially at the base of the skull. Give these areas a little extra attention and loving care. Move the scalp until it's loose and relaxed. Then brush your hair with a natural-bristle hairbrush for several minutes. Bend forward at the waist and brush from the base of the skull forward. Run the brush gently through the hair. This further massages the scalp and distributes the oil to the hair strands. Brush slowly, gently, and firmly.

Apply about 1 tablespoon of a hair oil made of extracts such as neem, wheat germ oil, chamomile, and rosemary. Run it through the hair, beginning at the scalp but concentrating on the ends. Comb the oil through with your fingers or a large-tooth comb. Cover your hair with a woolen hat or a cotton scarf and leave it on for at least an hour. If you want to protect the hat or the scarf from stains, put on a loose-fitting shower cap first. This will work up a little heat and help the oil penetrate more into the hair. The treatment may be left on overnight.

Shampoo thoroughly that night or the next morning. You may need an extra application of shampoo to remove excess oil. Rinse with diluted apple cider vinegar (2 quarts water to 2 tablespoons vinegar) before applying conditioner.

Step 12. Healing the Past, Embracing the Future: Write Your Biography

Special Project: Your Biography and Life Cycles

One of the principle benefits of this thirty-day period of Practicing Beauty is self-discovery, which is part of healing your inner beauty. Insights will arise naturally—as you prepare your meals, write in your journal, and walk in the park. But there is a powerful exercise you can do to obtain new and additional insights into your life. That exercise is to organize your life in seven-year periods and record the major events that occurred in each. Do this exercise over the entire month, adding new bits of information as they emerge. At the conclusion of the month, you will feel you know yourself better. Very likely, you'll also have a much clearer picture of where you are going and what you want to become.

Go through each year of your life and note important family events, such as celebrations, birthdays, vacations, trips, illnesses, deaths, and moves, or family lore. To stimulate your memory, ask a family member what he or she remembers about you.

Begin with the ages of birth to seven. Try to record at least five important events or trends that occurred during your childhood. Perhaps you have a particularly strong memory of your mother, or father, or of going to school. Perhaps you associate several important events with your first couple of years at school.

Do the same for each seven-year period of your life. When you are done, record the events as headlines on a U-shaped chart. The first thirty-two or thirty-three years or so form the downward part of the chart. This is the period in which you are grounding into your body, your nature, and your connection to the earth. After age

practicing beauty

Soups

Bean and Roasted Root Vegetable Soup

Butternut Squash Bisque

Curried Broccoli Soup

Greek Olive Soup with Beans and Rice

Green Soup

Lentil–Mushroom Stew

Lentil–Spinach Soup

Mixed–Pea Soup

Potato Leek–Miso Soup

Grains

Banana-Macadamia Pancakes with Orange Butter

Miso Porridge

Noachian Rice

Rice Pilaf

Spring Vegetables with Rice

Southwest Baked Millet

Whole-Wheat Linguine with Broccoli

Wild Rice Salad

Banana-Macadamia Pancakes with Orange Butter

Serves 2 to 4

Orange Butter

$1/2$ stick ($1/4$ cup) unsalted butter, softened
$1/2$ teaspoon finely grated orange zest
$1 1/2$ teaspoons fresh orange juice
$1/8$ teaspoon salt

Pancakes

1 cup all-purpose flour
$1/2$ cup whole-wheat flour
2 tablespoons sugar
1 teaspoon baking powder
$1/2$ teaspoon baking soda
$1/4$ teaspoon salt
1 cup buttermilk
$1/2$ cup milk
2 tablespoons unsalted butter, melted
2 large eggs
1 teaspoon vanilla extract
1 ripe banana, cut into thin slices
$1/2$ cup macadamia nuts, chopped

To Make the Orange Butter In a small bowl, stir together all the ingredients until well combined. Use softened or put back in the refrigerator to harden. The butter will keep in the refrigerator for up to a week.

To Make the Pancakes In a large bowl, whisk together the flours, sugar, baking powder, baking soda, and salt. In another bowl, whisk together the buttermilk, milk, melted butter, eggs, and vanilla. Combine the wet and the dry ingredients along with the banana and the nuts.

Pour $1/4$ cup batter per pancake onto a hot buttered griddle. Cook until bubbles appear on the surface and the undersides are golden brown, 1 to 2 minutes. Flip and cook until the other sides are golden brown as well. Transfer to a large plate and loosely cover with foil (or a skillet lid) to keep warm, then make more pancakes, brushing the skillet with butter for each batch. Serve with orange butter and maple syrup.

Miso Porridge

Serves 2 to 4

2 cups water
1 cup rolled oats
$1/4$ cup chopped dates
$1/4$ teaspoon cinnamon
$1/4$ teaspoon cardamom
2 teaspoons light miso
Maple syrup

In a large saucepan, bring the water to a boil, add the oats and dates, and reduce the heat to low. Cook for 5 to 10 minutes, or until the water is absorbed. Let the oatmeal cool to body temperature and then thoroughly stir the spices and miso into the warm cereal. Cover and let sit overnight at room temperature (about 70°F.). In the morning, cook in the oven at 300°F. for 20 minutes or on the stove over low heat until warm. Serve with maple syrup.

Variations:
Try with other types of rolled, cracked, or ground grains. The dates could be replaced with raisins, currants, dried cranberries, or dried plums. The spices could include nutmeg, allspice, or extracts such as almond or hazelnut. Honey, molasses, or rice syrup could replace the maple syrup.

Noachian Rice

Serves 4 to 6

$1^1/2$ cups brown basmati rice
2 cups fresh corn kernels
2 cups dark kidney beans, cooked
1 zucchini squash, diced
1 yellow squash, diced
1 onion, diced
1 teaspoon cinnamon
Salt and freshly ground black pepper

Cook the rice according to the package directions and let cool. In a large bowl, fold the corn and beans into the rice. Put the diced vegetables, rice mixture, and cinnamon in a large skillet and sauté in olive oil until the vegetables have softened. Add salt and pepper to taste and serve hot.

Rice Pilaf

Serves 2 to 4

2¹/₂ cups chicken stock or
   vegetable stock
¹/₄ cup coarsely chopped blanched
   almonds
¹/₄ cup pine nuts
2 tablespoons extra-virgin olive
   oil or butter
1 medium onion, finely chopped
1¹/₂ cups long-grain rice
One 3-inch cinnamon stick
Salt and freshly ground black
   pepper
¹/₄ cup golden raisins, plumped in
   warm water

In a large pot, bring the stock to a slow
simmer. In a saucepan over medium heat,
gently sauté the almonds and pine nuts in
the oil. Stir constantly. When the nuts are
lightly browned, remove them from the
pan and set aside. Add the onion to the
pan and cook, constantly stirring, until
the onion is transparent but not brown,
about 10 minutes. Add the rice and continue to cook, stirring constantly, until the
rice has a light brown color, about 5 minutes. Add the hot stock and cinnamon stick
and season with salt and pepper to taste.
Stir in the rice until all the ingredients are
well mixed, then lower the heat and cover.
Cook until all the liquid is absorbed, 15 to
20 minutes. Remove from the heat and set
aside for 5 minutes. Stir in the sautéed
nuts and drained raisins. Remove the cinnamon stick before serving.

Spring Vegetables with Rice

Serves 4 to 6

$1/4$ cup extra-virgin olive oil
1 medium onion, chopped
3 large garlic cloves, crushed
1 red sweet pepper, cut into strips
$1/2$ pound small red potatoes, halved
$1/2$ cup drained canned tomatoes, cut in chunks
5 cups light miso stock or vegetable broth
Pinch of saffron
Salt and freshly ground black pepper
$1/2$ pound fresh green beans, cut into pea-size lengths
4 small artichokes, quartered
1 pound fresh fava beans, shelled
$1/2$ pound fresh green peas, shelled
$1/2$ pound fresh asparagus, trimmed and cut into 2-inch lengths
2 cups medium-grain rice

In a large saucepan, heat the oil over medium heat. Add the onion, garlic, and red pepper strips and cook until soft but not brown, about 15 minutes. Add the potatoes and tomatoes and cook for another 10 minutes, until the potatoes are just soft. Add the stock, saffron, and salt and pepper to taste. When the stock begins to boil, add the green beans and artichokes. Reduce the heat slightly, cover, and cook for 10 more minutes. Add the favas, peas, and asparagus. Add the rice and mix well. Cook until the rice is tender, 15 to 20 minutes. Remove from the heat and let stand for about 5 minutes. Adjust the seasonings and serve.

Adzuki Beans and Delicata Squash

Serves 2 to 4

1 cup adzuki beans, soaked overnight
1-inch piece kombu*
1 delicata squash, cut into rings
1 tablespoon extra-virgin olive oil
Salt and freshly ground black pepper
$1/2$ cup diced onion
4 tablespoons South River Adzuki Miso

In a saucepan over medium heat, cook the beans with the kombu and 2 cups of water for $1^{1}/2$ hours, adding more water as needed. Preheat the oven to 350°F.

Coat the squash with the oil and salt and pepper to taste. Bake for 35 minutes. When the beans are soft, add the onion and miso. Continue cooking until all the liquid is absorbed. When the squash is ready, stuff it with the beans, bake for an additional 15 to 20 minutes, and serve.

*Kombu is a thick, dark brown sea vegetable that lends itself to flavoring soups and broths. It enhances the flavor of beans.

Bean, Corn, and Pumpkin Stew

Serves 6 to 8

1 cup pinto beans, soaked overnight
Salt
1 teaspoon cumin seeds
1 teaspoon dried oregano
1-inch cinnamon stick
3 cloves
4 tablespoons light olive oil
1 large onion, diced
2 garlic cloves, minced
1 tablespoon paprika
1 pound fresh tomatoes, peeled and seeded, juice reserved
3 cups pumpkin puree
2 cups light miso broth
$1^{1}/2$ cups corn kernels
2 green chiles, seeded and minced
Chopped parsley, for garnish

In a saucepan, cover the beans with water. Add $1/2$ teaspoon salt and cook for $1^{1}/2$ hours. Drain the beans and reserve the cooking liquid.

Heat a small skillet and toast the cumin seeds until fragrant. Add the oregano, cook for 5 seconds, and transfer to a plate. Grind the seeds in a spice mill with the cinnamon stick and cloves. In a large saucepan, heat the oil and sauté the onion over high heat for 1 minute, then lower the heat to medium. Add the garlic, paprika, and 1 teaspoon salt. Stir to combine, then add $1/2$ cup of the reserved bean broth and cook, stirring occasionally. Next add the tomatoes and cook for 5 minutes. Then add the pumpkin and 1 cup of the miso broth and continue cooking. After 30 minutes, add the corn, beans, and chiles. Thin with the reserved tomato juice and the remaining miso broth. Cook until the pumpkin is heated through, 15 to 20 minutes. Adjust the seasonings and garnish with parsley.

Beans with Olive Oil and Lemon

Serves 2 to 4

2 cups beans, soaked overnight
2 garlic cloves, minced
1 teaspoon salt
$1/2$ cup fresh lemon juice
$1/4$ cup extra-virgin olive oil
$1/2$ cup flat-leaf parsley
6 scallions
1 lemon, cut into wedges

Drain the beans and place them in a saucepan. Cover with fresh water and bring to a boil over medium heat. Simmer until the beans are tender, 1 to 2 hours, depending on the bean. When they are done, remove from the heat, drain, and reserve the cooking liquid.

Mash the garlic with the salt until it forms a paste. Add the lemon juice and mix well. Remove 1 cup of the beans and mash them with $1/2$ cup of the reserved bean liquid. Mix with the garlic and add the rest of the beans. Stir in the oil and pour on a serving plate. Garnish with the parsley, scallions, and lemon wedges. Serve with bread.

Black Bean and Pepper Salad

Serves 4 to 6

$1 1/4$ cups black beans, soaked overnight
1 bay leaf
$1/2$ teaspoon dried thyme
$1/2$ teaspoon dried oregano
1 teaspoon salt
$1/4$ cup vinaigrette
$1/2$ cup each red, yellow, and green bell
   pepper, diced small
$1/2$ red onion, finely chopped
1 celery stalk, diced small
1 green chile, seeded and minced
Chopped flat-leaf parsley, for garnish

In a saucepan, cover the beans with fresh water. Add the bay leaf and the herbs and bring to a boil. Add the salt, lower the heat, and simmer for 1 hour. Drain the beans.

Add the vinaigrette to the cooked beans while they are still warm, along with the peppers, onion, and celery. Stir everything together and adjust the seasonings. Add the minced chile. Garnish with parsley and serve at room temperature.

Cod with Sautéed Vegetables

Serves 4

1 tablespoon extra-virgin olive oil
4 cod fillets, 4 to 6 ounces each
Salt and freshly ground black pepper
2 tablespoons butter
2 cups shredded carrots
1 cup shredded zucchini
1 cup sliced mushrooms
1/4 cup chopped green onion
1 garlic clove, minced
1 tablespoon sesame seeds
Lemon slices

Preheat the oven to 350°F.

Coat a baking dish with the oil and add the cod fillets. Season lightly with salt and pepper and bake for 20 minutes.

In a sauté pan, heat the butter over medium heat. Add the carrots, zucchini, mushrooms, green onion, garlic, and sesame seeds and sauté lightly until tender, 5 to 7 minutes.

When the cod is finished, top with the sautéed vegetables, garnish with lemon, and serve.

Ginger-Sesame Alaska Salmon

Serves 2 to 4

1 small onion, sliced into rings
2 medium carrots, shredded or julienned
1 1/2 pounds Alaska salmon fillet
2 teaspoons grated fresh ginger
2 tablespoons seasoned rice vinegar, plus additional to taste
2 teaspoons toasted sesame oil
Salt and freshly ground black pepper
Fresh spinach leaves

Preheat the oven to 325°F.

Add the onion and carrots to a small covered baking dish, just big enough to hold the salmon fillet. Top with the salmon. In a small bowl, combine the ginger, rice vinegar, and oil. Pour over the salmon. Season with salt and pepper to taste. Cover and bake for 20 minutes, or until the fish flakes easily when tested with a fork.

Serve the salmon topped with onion rings and carrots on a bed of spinach. Sprinkle with additional seasoned rice vinegar.

Oven-Braised Fish

Serves 4 to 6

1½ to 2 pounds fish steaks such as salmon, hake, or halibut, each about 1 inch thick
Flour for dredging
3 tablespoons extra-virgin olive oil
2 large onions, halved and thinly sliced
1 garlic clove, minced
2 bay leaves
1 teaspoon salt
½ teaspoon paprika
Juice of ½ lemon

Preheat the oven to 375°F.

Lightly dredge the fish steaks in a little flour, shaking them to remove any excess. In a sauté pan over medium heat, sauté the steaks in 2 tablespoons of the oil for 3 to 4 minutes on each side. Transfer to a glass baking dish and lay them flat, without overlapping. Add the onions, garlic, bay leaves, salt, and the remaining tablespoon of oil to the same sauté pan. Stir to mix well. Cover and cook for 15 minutes. Remove the bay leaves and add the paprika and lemon juice. Cover the fish with the onions and bake for 20 minutes.

Shrimp, Fennel, and Quinoa Pilaf

Serves 4

2 fennel stalks with fronds
3 tablespoons extra-virgin olive oil
1 medium onion, chopped
1 garlic clove, minced
½ teaspoon cayenne pepper
1¼ cups quinoa, washed well
1 ripe tomato, peeled, seeded, chopped, and drained
2 cups water or chicken broth
2 teaspoons Worcestershire sauce
½ teaspoon salt
1 pound medium shrimp, peeled and deveined
Freshly grated nutmeg

Preheat the oven to 350°F.

Chop the fennel stalks and fronds separately. Set aside. In a 2-quart ovenproof casserole over medium heat, heat the oil. Stir in the onion, garlic, and cayenne, lower the heat, and sauté until the onion is tender, about 10 minutes. Add the fennel and quinoa and sauté for 2 minutes more. Add the tomato, water, Worcestershire sauce, and salt and bring to a simmer. Cover and bake for 25 minutes, or until the liquid is absorbed.

Remove from the oven. Uncover, fluff with a fork, and stir in the shrimp. Cover and let stand for 10 minutes. The heat will cook the shrimp. Sprinkle with nutmeg and chopped fennel fronds. Serve hot or at room temperature.

Mushroom and Beef Stroganoff

Serves 4 to 6

3 tablespoons olive oil
1/2 large onion, chopped
1 clove garlic, diced
1/2 cup burgundy wine
1 pound beef, cubed
1 pound white button mushrooms, sliced
2 portobello mushrooms, diced
3/4 cup oat milk or soy milk
3 tablespoons tamari
1 teaspoon freshly ground black pepper
2 bay leaves
1 tablespoon fresh thyme or 1 teaspoon
  dried thyme
1 pound cooked linguine

In a large sauté pan, heat the oil over medium-low heat. Add the onion and garlic and cook slowly until brown, about 5 minutes. Deglaze the pan with the wine as the onion and garlic cook. Add the beef and sauté for 20 minutes at medium-low heat. Add the mushrooms and sauté for 2 minutes, until the mushrooms are limp. Add the oat milk, tamari, pepper, bay leaves, and thyme. Simmer for 10 minutes; the mixture will thicken. Serve over cooked linguine.

Beef Stew

Serves 6 to 8

1 pound stewing beef, cut into chunks
Whole-wheat flour for dredging
2 tablespoons extra-virgin olive oil
2 medium onions, chopped
4 cups mixed vegetables*
1 cup red wine
1 tablespoon fresh thyme
1 tablespoon fresh sage
1 tablespoon fresh oregano
1/4 cup chopped parsley
1 teaspoon salt
1 teaspoon freshly ground black pepper
2 potatoes, cut into chunks

Coat the stewing beef in whole-wheat flour and sauté in the oil until browned. Add the onions to the pan and cook for an additional 5 minutes. Add to a slow cooker along with the seasonal vegetables (parsnips are an excellent addition). Add the wine and 2 cups of water, along with the chopped fresh herbs, salt, and pepper. Cover and cook on low for 5 hours. Add the potatoes and cook for another 1 to 1 1/2 hours, until tender. Adjust the seasonings. Serve with red wine and rustic bread.

*Use carrots, onions, parsnips, or any seasonal vegetables.

Chicken with Coconut-Curry Sauce

Serves 2 to 4

1 cup unsweetened coconut milk
$1/4$ cup fresh lime juice
2 teaspoons lime zest
$1/4$ cup brown sugar or honey
$1/4$ cup chopped scallion
$1/4$ cup cilantro
2 teaspoons curry powder
$1/4$ teaspoon sea salt
$3^{1}/_{2}$- to 4-pound whole chicken

Preheat the oven to 400°F.

Combine all the ingredients except the chicken in a bowl and whisk thoroughly. Coat the chicken with half of the mixture and place in a roasting pan with a rack. Roast for 1 hour. Baste with the remaining sauce. The chicken is cooked when an instant-read thermometer registers 170°F.

Chicken with a Miso-Honey Glaze

Serves 4

4 tablespoons South River Sweet-Tasting
  Brown Rice Miso
2 tablespoons honey
2 tablespoons apple cider vinegar
2 garlic cloves, minced
$1/2$ cup olive oil

2 large boneless chicken breasts, cut in half
Canola oil

To Prepare the Glaze Blend the miso, honey, vinegar, and garlic in a blender on high speed. Reduce the blender to medium speed and slowly add the oil to produce a thick, creamy glaze.

Place the chicken on a dish and cover thoroughly with the glaze. In a sauté pan, heat the oil over medium-high heat. Sauté the chicken on each side for $2^{1}/_{2}$ minutes, then reduce the heat, cover, and simmer for 25 minutes until the juices run clear when the breasts are pricked with a fork.

Chicken with Olive Rice

Serves 4

2 tablespoons butter
$1/4$ teaspoon salt
$1/8$ teaspoon freshly ground black pepper
$1/2$ teaspoon dried thyme
$1/4$ teaspoon poultry seasoning
$1/4$ teaspoon paprika
Juice of 1 lemon
2 large boneless chicken breasts, cut in half

1 cup brown basmati rice
1 cup stuffed olives

Preheat the oven to 350°F.

In a sauté pan over medium heat, melt the butter. Add the seasonings and lemon juice and heat. Place the chicken in a baking pan and pour the lemon-butter mixture over the chicken. Bake for 1 hour. While the chicken is cooking, bring 2 cups of water to a boil and add the rice. Return to a boil, reduce to a simmer, cover, and cook for 20 to 30 minutes.

The chicken is cooked when the juices run clear when the breasts are pricked with a fork. When the chicken is done, pour off the juices into a measuring cup and skin off the fat. Add the remaining juices and olives to the rice. Serve the chicken pieces over the rice.

Chicken Sausage, Chard, and Beans over Polenta

Serves 4

3 tablespoons extra-virgin olive oil
1 onion, diced
2 garlic cloves, minced
Prepared polenta
2 chicken sausages, cooked and cut into pieces
1 can cannellini beans, soaked overnight and cooked until tender
1 small red bell pepper, roasted
5 whole cooked tomatoes
1 bunch Swiss chard, chopped
Basil
Parsley
Salt and freshly ground black pepper

In a large skillet, heat 1 tablespoon of the oil over medium heat. Add the onion and garlic. Sauté for 2 minutes until the onion is translucent and the garlic is lightly browned.

Preheat the oven to 250°F. Slice the polenta in $1/2$-inch-thick pieces. Heat another tablespoon of the oil in a large sauté pan over medium heat and sauté the polenta on both sides for $2 1/2$ minutes each until they are lightly browned. Once the polenta is finished, transfer the pieces to a plate and keep warm in the oven.

Cut the sausages into slices and cook in a sauté pan until browned, about 10 minutes. Transfer to a plate and keep warm in the oven. Heat the remaining tablespoon of oil in the same sauté pan over medium heat. Add the beans, pepper, tomatoes, chard, and seasonings. Cook until the chard is wilted and tender, about 10 minutes. Add the sausages to the mixture and serve over the warm polenta.

Grilled Chicken in a Lemon Marinade

Serves 5

1 $\frac{1}{2}$ tablespoons white peppercorns
2 teaspoons cumin seeds
1 teaspoon coriander seeds
$\frac{1}{2}$ teaspoon cinnamon
12 garlic cloves
2 teaspoons salt
1 cup finely chopped onion
2 tablespoons grated lemon zest
$\frac{1}{4}$ cup fresh lemon juice
$\frac{1}{4}$ cup canola oil
$\frac{1}{4}$ cup chopped parsley
5 pounds chicken pieces

In a sauté pan over medium heat, toast the peppercorns, cumin, coriander, and cinnamon, stirring until fragrant, about 1 minute. Grind the spices. In a blender, puree the spices, garlic, salt, onion, lemon zest, juice, oil, and parsley. Put the marinade and chicken pieces in a ziplock bag and store in the refrigerator overnight.

Remove the chicken from the bag, allowing any excess marinade to drip away. Discard the balance of the marinade. Grill the chicken over medium heat for 25 minutes or bake at 325°F. for 30 to 40 minutes. The chicken is done when the juices run clear when pricked with a fork.

Stuffed Peppers

Serves 6

1 pound ground beef, ground lamb, or ground buffalo
2 tablespoons extra-virgin olive oil
1 medium onion, peeled and finely chopped
1 small can tomato paste
1 cup beef stock or vegetable stock
$\frac{1}{2}$ teaspoon dried thyme
$\frac{1}{2}$ teaspoon dried rosemary
$\frac{1}{2}$ teaspoon dried oregano
2 cups cooked brown rice
$\frac{1}{4}$ cup lightly toasted pine nuts
Salt and freshly ground black pepper
6 green bell peppers, stemmed, sliced in half lengthwise, and seeded
1 cup Parmesan cheese or Cheddar cheese

Preheat the oven to 350°F.

In a heavy skillet, brown the meat in the oil for 10 to 15 minutes. Add the onion, tomato paste, stock, and herbs. Bring to a boil and cook until the liquid has reduced by about half. Remove from the heat and stir in the rice, pine nuts, and salt and pepper to taste. Set the peppers in a buttered ceramic or glass dish, fill each pepper half with stuffing, and top with cheese. Bake for 45 minutes, until golden and bubbly.

Dairy

Cheese Soufflé

Basic Omelet

Pepper Quiche

Cheese Soufflé

Serves 6

6 tablespoons butter
6 tablespoons unbleached flour
1 cup cream mixed with 1 cup water,
   warmed
6 large eggs, separated, at room temperature
1 cup grated Gouda, Mahon, or Monterey
   Jack cheese
1 cup grated Parmesan cheese
Salt and freshly ground black pepper

Preheat the oven to 400°F.

In a heavy saucepan, melt the butter over medium heat. Add the flour and stir with a wooden spoon until the butter turns light brown. Gradually add the cream and water mixture, beating with a wire whisk until the mixture thickens. Remove from the heat and stir in the egg yolks, one at a time, and then the cheeses. Season with salt and pepper to taste. Place the egg whites in a glass or stainless-steel bowl and add a pinch of salt and beat until stiff. Gently fold the egg yolks into the egg whites and pour the mixture into a buttered 2-quart soufflé dish. Place in the preheated oven, lower the heat to 350°F., and bake for 40 minutes. Serve immediately.

Basic Omelet

Serves 2

4 large eggs at room temperature
Dash of hot sauce
Pinch of sea salt
2 tablespoons butter

Crack the eggs into a bowl. Add 3 tablespoons of water, the hot sauce, and salt and blend with a wire whisk. In a cast-iron skillet over medium heat, melt the butter. Add the eggs to the pan. Tip the pan to allow the eggs to cover the entire surface. Cook for several minutes over medium-low heat until the underside is lightly browned. Lift up one side with a spatula and fold the omelet in half. Reduce the heat and cook briefly, about 30 seconds. Slide the omelet onto a warm plate and serve.

Variation: Herb Omelet

Add 1 tablespoon finely chopped fresh herb, such as parsley, chives, dill, or thyme, into the egg mixture.

Pepper Quiche

Serves 4 to 6

I recommend purchasing whole-wheat pastry shells unless you're comfortable making your own piecrusts. You may use red, yellow, or orange peppers, or a combination.

1 prepared whole-wheat 9-inch piecrust
2 peppers, seeded and cut into thin strips
1 onion, finely sliced
2 tablespoons extra-virgin olive oil
3 large egg yolks
$1/2$ cup crème fraîche or heavy cream
Sea salt and freshly ground black pepper
1 cup freshly grated Parmesan cheese or
    Cheddar cheese

Preheat the oven to 350°F. Bake the piecrust for 20 minutes. Remove from the oven and let cool. Meanwhile, in a sauté pan over medium heat, sauté the peppers and onion in the oil until soft, about 6 minutes. Remove from the heat. In a mixing bowl, beat the yolks with the cream, seasonings, and half of the cheese. Spread the peppers over the baked crust and pour the egg mixture over. Top with the remaining cheese and bake for about 30 minutes, until golden.

Variation: Artichoke and Roasted Red Peppers or Sun-dried Tomatoes

Substitute $1/2$ pound sliced artichokes and $1/2$ cup either roasted red peppers or sun-dried tomatoes. Sauté in a mixture of 2 tablespoons butter and 2 tablespoons olive oil and proceed with the recipe.

Variation: Zucchini Quiche

Omit the peppers. Use 2 small zucchini, cut into thin strips. Mix with 1 tablespoon sea salt and drain in a colander for 30 minutes. Rinse and squeeze dry in a paper towel. Spread the zucchini over the baked crust and proceed with the recipe.

Fresh Figs and Honey

Serves 2 to 4

4 ounces ricotta
3 ounces cream cheese, softened
2 tablespoons milk
18 ripe figs
2 teaspoons chopped mint
Honey

In a bowl, beat together the ricotta, cream cheese, and milk until smooth. Chill in the refrigerator for 2 hours. Wipe the figs with a damp paper towel and slice off the stems. Cut a cross at the top to about $^3/_4$ inch. Squeeze at the base of the fig to open up the top. Spoon a bit of the cheese mixture into each fig. Sprinkle with mint and drizzle with honey. Serve on small plates or in dessert cups or bowls.

Frozen Berry-Banana Parfait

Serves 2

Berries in season are ideal. Otherwise, look for good frozen organic berries.

2 large bananas, peeled and frozen
2 tablespoons vanilla yogurt
1 teaspoon maple syrup
$^1/_2$ cup berries

Cut the bananas into chunks and puree with the yogurt and 2 tablespoons of water in a blender until creamy. Add the maple syrup and pulse again. Put a spoonful of berries in the bottom of two parfait glasses and top with about one-third of the banana mixture. Repeat the layers, ending with the berries. Serve immediately.

Fruit Smoothie

Serves 2

1 cup yogurt
1 cup orange juice
1 banana, frozen
$1/4$ fresh pineapple
1 apple
3 to 5 ice cubes

Put all the ingredients in a blender and blend until smooth. Add more juice if the liquid is too thick. Pour into glasses and serve.

Ginger-Pear Pie

Serves 4 to 6

Filling

5 cups sliced pears
3 tablespoons fresh lemon juice
$1/2$ cup sugar
2 tablespoons flour
1 teaspoon lemon peel
2 teaspoons minced fresh ginger

Topping

$1/2$ cup flour
$1/2$ cup sugar
$1/2$ teaspoon cinnamon
$1/8$ teaspoon mace
$1/4$ cup butter

10-inch prepared pie shell

Preheat the oven to 375°F.

To Make the Filling Sprinkle the pears with the lemon juice. In a bowl, combine the sugar, flour, lemon peel, and ginger and mix with the pears.

To Make the Topping In another bowl, cut together the flour, sugar, spices, and butter with two knives or a pastry cutter, until the mixture resembles coarse meal.

Put the pears in the pie shell and cover with the topping. Bake for 25 minutes with the edges covered and for another 25 minutes with the edges uncovered, until golden brown.

Pears Poached in Vanilla Syrup

Serves 6

$^1/_2$ cup sugar
$^1/_2$ vanilla bean, split lengthwise
$3^1/_2$-inch strips lemon peel
6 firm pears, peeled, seeded, and cut in half

In a medium saucepan, bring $2^1/_2$ cups of water to a boil with the sugar, vanilla bean, and lemon peel. Stir to dissolve the sugar; then lower the heat and simmer for 2 to 3 minutes. Add the pears and cook them gently until they are translucent around the edges. Remove the pears from the syrup and put them in a bowl. Strain the syrup. Pour over the fruit and refrigerate until well chilled. Serve in individual dessert cups.

Quinoa and Date Pudding

Serves 4 to 6

3 tablespoons butter
Shortbread cookie crumbs
$^1/_2$ cup packed light brown sugar
2 large eggs, lightly beaten
1 cup milk
1 tablespoon vanilla extract
1 teaspoon cinnamon
Pinch of salt
2 cups cooked quinoa
$^1/_2$ cup chopped dates
$^1/_2$ cup toasted hazelnuts
Nutmeg

Preheat the oven to 325°F. Using 1 tablespoon of the butter, grease a $1^1/_2$-quart baking dish or individual ramekins. Coat the buttered surface with cookie crumbs. Set aside.

In a large bowl, cream the remaining butter and brown sugar. Stir in the eggs, milk, vanilla, cinnamon, and salt until blended. Add the quinoa, dates, and hazelnuts and mix thoroughly. Pour the custard mixture into a baking dish and grate a little nutmeg over the top. Bake for 50 minutes, or until just barely set. Remove from the heat and let cool for 10 minutes. To serve, spoon from the dish or loosen the edges with a knife and invert onto a serving plate.

Raspberry Custard

Serves 2 to 4

3 tablespoons cornstarch or arrowroot flour
1 quart milk
$1/2$ cup maple syrup
1 cup raspberries
Mint leaves

In a medium saucepan, dissolve the cornstarch in 3
tablespoons of water. Add to the milk along with the
maple syrup and bring to a boil, stirring occasionally.
Reduce the heat and simmer for 3 minutes. Cool slightly
in a bowl and gently stir in the raspberries. Pour the
pudding into individual custard cups and chill for 1 to 2
hours. Garnish with additional raspberries and mint
leaves before serving.

Rice Pudding

Serves 4

1 quart milk
1 whole cinnamon stick (about 3 inches)
$1/2$ teaspoon crushed cardamom seeds
$1/8$ teaspoon whole cloves
1 cup white basmati rice
2 tablespoons almond butter
2 tablespoons honey
Pinch of salt

In a medium saucepan, bring the milk, cinnamon stick,
cardamom seeds, and cloves to a boil. Add the rice,
cover, and reduce the heat. Simmer for 1 hour. Discard
the cinnamon stick and cloves. Stir in the almond butter,
honey, and salt. Serve warm or chilled.

Acknowledgments

I would like to thank the following people who supported me with love and patience while I was working on this new venture:

First of all my family: my husband, Clifford, and our three children, John, Emilio, and Rossibel, for their presence in my life. Kelly Farrell for her nourishing meals and menus. A big thanks to my agent, Linda Roghaar, for encouraging me to "just do it," and to Tom Monte for putting my thoughts to paper. I could never have accomplished this project without the the professional and creative work of my coworkers at Dr. Hauschka Skin Care, Inc., who have created a fabulous team I'm proud to be part of. I would especially like to thank Mirran Raphaely, Betsy Strickland, Jill Price Marshall, Geoffrey Rice, Deborah Hubresch, Kathy White, and Robin Gingrass for finding time for all my last-minute requests. Thanks to Marie Hubonette for her friendship and contributions to the biography/life-cycle work that reminds us of the importance of each individual destiny. I'm forever grateful to Sandy Littell for her ceaseless commitment to the photo edits, and to Stacey Brosnan of Femsurge for her advice on topical treatments. Thanks to Sebastian Parsons for sharing his photos with us.

Thanks to WALA Heilmittel, the manufacturers of Dr. Hauschka Skin Care, for bringing the gift of holistic medicine and skin care to the world. I would especially like to thank Dr. Rudolf Hauschka for his pioneering work with natural substances and for his vision to bring a new business paradigm into the world. Thanks, too, to Karl Kossmann for helping to make Dr. Hauschka's dream a reality and for his willingness to share his experiences with me in wonderful interviews.

I cannot thank Elisabeth Sigmund enough for devoting her life to developing products and a therapeutic treatment for the contemporary woman on a path to self-knowledge. I dedicate this book to Elisabeth, and look forward to continued collaboration.

I am most grateful to Rudolf Steiner for anthroposophy, his great gift to the world. It is a source of daily inspiration for those of us working to awaken beauty.

Index

Index of Recipes

Photo Credits

Art and Commerce, William Abranowicz: 131

Tara Baxter: 90, 91, 93

Sandra Costantini: 46 (below), 123, 125

Digital Vision, Veer: 18 (above), 73, 100 (below), 113

Furnald/Gray: 4, 7, 8 (above), 8 (center), 8 (below left), 13, 15, 16, 17, 22 (left), 24, 25, 36, 37, 38, 42, 43, 47, 50 (right), 51 (left), 55 (below), 65, 66, 67, 74, 86 (below), 95, 104, 105, 122 (above), 141, 143

Getty Images, Amy Neunsinger: 114

Getty Images, Botanica, Jennifer Cheung: 60 (above)

Getty Images, FoodPix, Sang An: 150

Getty Images, FoodPix, Benjamin F. Fink, Jr.: 192

Getty Images, FoodPix, Rob Fiocca: 160, 180

Getty Images, FoodPix, Richard Jung: 163, 196

Getty Images, FoodPix, Alison Miksch: 39

Getty Images, FoodPix, Ngoc Minh Ngo: 168

Getty Images, FoodPix, Lisa Romerein: 154

Getty Images, FoodPix, Mark Thomas: 146, 156, 177

Getty Images, FoodPix, Simon Watson: 185, 201

Getty Images, FoodPix, Cheryl Zibisky: 164

Getty Images, The Image Bank, Jean Louis Batt: 2

Getty Images, The Image Bank, Jason Homa: 139

Getty Images, The Image Bank, Rita Moss: 148

Getty Images, The Image Bank, Roger Wright: 85

Getty Images, Photonica, Neo Vision: 172

Getty Images, Stone Collection, April: 52

Getty Images, Stone Collection, Brian Bailey: 126

Getty Images, Stone Collection, Judith Haeusler: 120

Getty Images, Stone Collection, Bob Thomas: 144

Getty Images, Stone Collection, Jerome Tisue: 63

Getty Images, Taxi, Robin Macdougall: 186

Paul S. Grand: 46 (above)

Image100, Veer: 119, 122 (below)

Lightworks: 70, 71, 76

Sandy Littell: 19, 23 (right), 28, 33

Amy Neunsinger: 6

Photo Alto, Veer: 26, 61, 108

Photodisc, Veer: 40, 44, 133

Photography by Janine Hosegood for Cape Photographic / Elysia Natural Skin Care: 18 (below), 23 (left), 78 (below), 79, 80, 96

Deniz Saylan: 14, 34, 55 (above), 60 (below), 64, 69, 86 (above), 88, 110, 117, 118, 136, 140

Jonathan Sherrill: 32, 101, 107

Phil Stiles: 9 (above), 10

Courtesy of WALA Heilmittel GmbH: 8 (below right), 9 (below), 22 (center), 22 (right), 35, 48, 49, 50 (left), 50 (center), 51 (right), 53, 56, 57, 58, 77, 78 (above), 87, 94, 98, 100 (above), 103, 106, 132, 134